1
Infinitesimal
Dose

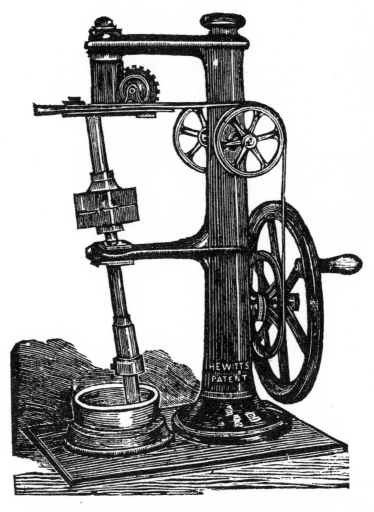

An apparatus for trituration

Dr Colin B. Lessell

MB, BS (Lond), BDS (Lond), MRCS (Eng), LRCP (Lond)

The Infinitesimal Dose

The scientific roots of homoeopathy

INDEX COMPILED
BY LYN GREENWOOD

SAFFRON WALDEN
THE C.W. DANIEL COMPANY LIMITED

First published in Great Britain in 1994
by The C.W. Daniel Company Limited
1 Church Path, Saffron Walden
Essex, CB10 1JP, England

© Colin B. Lessell 1994

ISBN 0 85207 276 7

This book is printed on part-recycled paper

Designed by Tim McPhee
Produced by Book Production Consultants
Typeset by Cambridge Photosetting Services
Printed and bound by Biddles, Guildford

Contents

*I*llustrations

Acknowledgements

I should like to acknowledge the valuable pharmaceutical advice given to me by Malcolm Fairbrother, Tony Pinkus and the professional staff of Ainsworth's Pharmacy, without which the text could only have been completed with great difficulty. As ever, I extend my gratitude to the British Homoeopathic Library at Glasgow for identifying and supplying relevant material; and to Dr Peter Fisher for pointing me in the direction of some informative papers. Finally, I should like to thank British Airways for their contribution to the abandonment of my recent proposed trip to China; as a result of which, inspired by the beauty of the great stone walls of Shropshire, I was able to complete the manuscript ahead of schedule.

Dr C.B. Lessell
MB, BS, BDS, MRCS, LRCP

Introduction

This book is for the student of homoeopathy; a term I use to embrace all those who have some knowledge of the subject, and who wish to develop further in that direction, including the ever-learning practitioner, and, not least of all, myself.

It is one man's attempt to clarify and explain the physicochemical foundations of *potentisation* and *posology* (dosage) within homoeopathic medicine. As will become apparent, the idea of 'water memory', so sacred to the homoeopathists but ridiculed by others, is closely related to that of the 'occult' storage of energy by the same substance. If nothing else, the theory (or hypothesis, if you prefer) which is brought before you will serve as a sensible basis for future discussion and argument; for, who can argue with the homoeopathist who merely shrugs his shoulders when asked the physical nature of remedies in general?

Throughout the verbal text, the superscript numerals correspond to particular works of reference (papers and books) enumerated in the bibliography, and to which I have personally referred; each author's unknowing stimulus being gratefully acknowledged. The conceptual basis being more important than the numerical, any mathematical propositions and statements made should not be regarded as a deterrent to the understanding of basic principles by those not so inclined.

Playing the Devil's advocate

In purely mechanistic terms, *potentisation* means the process of serial dilution and serial succussion peculiar to homoeopathy. More fundamentally, however, it may be defined as the transference of medicinal information to, and its amplification within, a diluent. *Posology is* the methodology of *dosage* in general, but in this case with reference to homoeopathy in particular.

Unfortunately, the whole matter of homoeopathic posology would appear to be in a state of chaotic disorder. Patient sensitivity aside, one practitioner treats a bruise with Arnica 200c, another with Arnica 6c, and a third uses 30c (pronouncing that he uses that potency 'for everything'). In more generalised disorders, some start with a few doses of 10M (10000c); others, perhaps more cautiously, advocate a 6c of the appropriate remedy every 12 hours. To this must be added the fact that there are three standard scales of serial dilution (centesimal, decimal and fifty millesimal), each with its own adherents, and, beyond that, an enormous variation in the actual material amounts given. One practitioner may give a single tiny globule the size of a pin-head, another advocates a pilule fifty times the size, and yet another recommends one full drop of liquid potency. Some say a child should have one pilule, and adults two. Others refute this, and state that the dose for a mouse is the same as that for an elephant. Surely, nothing could be more contrived to deter the initiate.

At the root of this dilemma has been a failure to supply a reasonable and cohesive theory of the process of potentisation. For, whereas the dictionary defines posology as the *science* of dosage, homoeopathic posology appears to rely on an inability to define not only the exact nature of its remedies but also, therefore, their concrete magnitude. Perhaps naturally, the more recent confirmatory statistical clinical analyses of remedial action have fortified the homoeopathists; and upon these techniques, as laudable as they may be, they have concentrated their efforts, rather than the search for the scientific basis of their practice. In so doing, and in constantly asserting a 'natural law[15]', the Law of Similars (*Similia similibus curentur*), as the foundation of their therapy, they feel that they have elevated their *art* to a *science;* but what science is it that knows neither what it dispenses, nor in which quantity?

The enigma is further exacerbated when we come to examine the practices of homoeopathic pharmacy. In the preparation of liquid potencies, some pharmacies employ ten succussions per dilution, and others twenty. Hahnemann advocated two, and finally settled upon one hundred; although admittedly he did change his method of dilution to match the larger number of succussions. Most say that distilled water should be the aqueous basis for the diluent, and tap-water is acceptable to a minority of others. The alcoholic strength of the diluent employed in serial dilution varies from 15 to 95%, according to economics and apparently according to the whim of the pharmacy. The drive for respectability and 'science', however, has engendered a movement within the EEC to standardise pharmaceutical methods in homoeopathy. Indeed, with regard to fundamental matters, such as the preparation of mother tinctures, this is a most commendable approach. However, when we come to the sticky matter of potentisation, how will it be possible to standardise the method in the light of ignorance of its physicochemical foundation? Whichever method might be chosen would be totally arbitrary.

The problem, in a sense, begins with Hahnemann himself, who through his genius developed his methods both intuitively and empirically. What might have appeared in the 19th Century to be scientific explanations of his methodology are no longer valid in the modern world; a thing, of course, for which he cannot be criticised. Indeed, intuition and empiricism in homoeopathy have been its saving grace over the years, not to mention its realism and pragmatism. But one thing it has not been is a *science*. Strangely perhaps, it survives because it *works*.

In all fairness, these matters must be put in perspective. Orthodox medicine, or *allopathy* as it is termed, is highly scientific in its reductionism. However, it peers down the microscope at a cell, but fails to see the man to whom it has belonged. It prostitutes its science by disallowing an ingress of holistic art. It frequently fails to see that one disease may be linked to another of remote or current chronology, and prescribes a number of unassociated medicines. It supports itself with an hierarchy of technical investigative strength and diagnostic imbalance.

The truth of the matter, however, is that despite the prodigious vagaries of both its pharmaceutics and posology, homoeopathy has been *enormously successful*; and whilst making no claims to replace the totality of its orthodox antagonist, does in fact constitute a serious and often superior rival. Nevertheless, we are not absolved from comprehending better what we do. Can we, 150 years or so beyond his death, do better than Hahnemann in his quasi-scientific explanation of the phenomenon of potentisation[16]:

> 'It becomes uncommonly evident that the material part [of an original substance] by means of such dynamisation [potentisation]...will ultimately dissolve into its individual spirit-like (conceptual) essence. In its crude state, therefore, it may be considered to consist really only of this undeveloped conceptual essence.'

Organon, 6th edition, Section 270 (footnote)

Personally, I think we can.

ELEMENT II

From chaos to curry

If there were one thing in common life that might represent the infinite, it would be the *chicken curry*. With a few basic spices, the repertoire of alternative recipes is seemingly endless. But, at the conclusion of cooking, we mostly have something that is identifiable as a chicken curry. Despite the considerable differences in methods of potentisation, in terms of both technique and scale of dilution, we always seem to produce a remedy of recognisable clinical properties; although some preparations appear more potent than others. Perhaps naively, some people mistakenly believe that a 6c of Pulsatilla from pharmacy A is of necessity the same as that produced by pharmacy B. It is true that both will have the 'flavour' of Pulsatilla, but there may well be a considerable difference in therapeutic strength. Until techniques are standardised, this will ever be so, and they cannot be sensibly standardised until we have a reasonable understanding of the fundamental chemistry of potentisation. Producing a uniform, albeit mundane, canned curry is apparently a lot easier.

When we come to serve our guests, there are a limited number of acceptable modes of presentation. We may dispense our remedies in Balti fashion, as they come, straight from the 'pan'; that is to say, in liquid potency (but sometimes watered down). Alternatively, we may place them on beds of sugar of various types, and give them as impregnated granules, pilules, tablets or powders. In more avant-garde establishments, they appear as creams, suppositories, injections or inhalations. Garnishing and presentation, however, are generally more to do with psychology and convenience than therapy as such.

What is far more important is the correct satiation of the physiological appetite. We may eat little and often with chopsticks (low potency technique); or, entering the age of the quick and easy, we may administer capsules of curry concentrate at infrequent intervals (high potency technique). Different techniques suit different individuals. Those with less robust constitutions are better suited to the 'Chinese' method. Overdosage, with the dire consequences of 'curry poisoning', is obviously more likely in the capsular approach; an over-zealous dose being the straw to break the metabolic back, with the production of what is euphemistically referred to as *homoeopathic aggravation*. Chopsticks are safer in this respect.

Let us now briefly review the three standard scales of homoeopathic serial dilution, with particular reference to the molecular (or ionic) presence of any *original substance*, be it arsenic or otherwise. The *centesimal* scale (denoted by c, cH or C) involves serial dilutions of 1 in 100. The *decimal* scale (denoted by x or D), more popular in Germany, requires serial dilutions of 1 in 10. The *fifty millesimal* (or *LM*) scale, based on serial dilutions of 1 in 50,000 (though using 3c as its initial base), grows in favour, and employs one hundred succussions per dilution, as opposed to the ten or so of its rivals. The *safe point*, as we might term it, is that stage of serial dilution where the concentration of any original substance is so low that, in normal therapeutic dosage, there is negligible toxicity; even with regard to the most virulent poisons. This point, for practical purposes and according to scale, may be taken to be 6c, 11x, or LM1. Furthermore, dilutions beyond 12c, 24x and LM4 are unlikely to contain any molecules of original substance whatsoever (except, perhaps, the odd one occasionally). These matters will be material to our analysis of the process of potentisation.

For the moment, it is important to realise that, except for the initial processing of insoluble substances, all three of the above scales are prepared by essentially the same method; that is to say, serial dilution in ethanol (ethyl alcohol)-water and succussion within a glass vial. They must all, therefore, produce something very similar, but with subtle quantitative and qualitative variations, enough to produce discernible therapeutic differences. Whilst accepting that LM potencies might well be the mildest and most thorough in action, often producing a profound and unaggravated cure, what justifies the inexplicit statement, as some would make, that they are also 'the most energised'? Without a comprehension of the processes involved, edicts such as this are fairly meaningless.

As you are aware, not all substances are initially soluble in ethanol-water, and these must be prepared by the method of prolonged grinding with lactose (milk sugar) in a mortar and pestle or some equivalent device. In any event, the 3c or 6x *trituration* of any substance is always soluble in ethanol-water, whatever its nature, and potentisation proceeds thereafter in the liquid phase.

Whereas many are prepared to accept that the diluent may hold some message characteristic of the original substance, the idea that dilution increases that effect has, not surprisingly, met with much disbelief on the part of non-homoeopaths. We, of course, feel that serial succussion distinguishes potentisation from simple or progressive dilution. Moreover, whilst correctly maintaining that dilution is required to render a medicine non-toxic, many homoeopathists also maintain that serial dilution is *essential* for the magnification of the medicinal message. However, from Hahnemann's writings we see that he did not believe that this was so:

> 'In order to have a determinate rule for the moderate developement of power of the fluid medicines, multiplied experience and observation have led me to retain two shakes for every vial, in preference to a greater number, which had previously been used, but which developed the energy in too great a degree. On the contrary, there are homoeopathists who, in their visits to the sick, carry about their persons the medicines in a fluid state, which, they nevertheless affirm, do not in time become increased in energy by the frequent agitation to which they are subjected. This declaration, however, betrays on their part the want of talent for accurate observation. I dissolved a grain of natron [native sesquicarbonate of soda] in half an ounce of a mixture of water and a little alcohol, poured the solution into a little vial, which was thereby filled two-thirds, and shook it uninterruptedly for half an hour. By this agitation, the fluid attained an energy equal to that of the thirtieth dilution.'

Organon, 1st American edition, section 270 (footnote)

What he did perceive, however, was the *desirability* of dilution[16]:

> 'But with so small a diluting medium as 100 to 1 of the medicine, if many succussions by means of a powerful machine are forced into it, medicines are then developed which, especially in the higher degrees of dynamisation [potentisation], act almost immediately, but with furious, even dangerous, violence, especially in weakly patients, without having a lasting, mild reaction of the vital principle.'

Organon, 6th edition, Section 270 (footnote)

In Hahnemann's view, serial dilution qualifies the development of the medicinal message engendered by succussion. It retards its aggressive evolution, so as to provide a gentle gradation of ascending therapeutic levels, which are the *potencies*, reaching the zenith of 'perfection' in the LM scale (although Hahnemann, had he lived longer, might well have found an even 'more perfect' method). The idea that dilution increases the 'energy' of a remedy may stem from Hahnemann's unfortunate use of the word *power* (or its derivative *powerful*):

'...the preparations thus produced [the LM potencies], I have found after many laborious experiments and counter-experiments, to be the most powerful and at the same time mildest in action, i.e. the most perfected...'

'...the material part of the medicine is lessened with each degree of dynamisation [potentisation] 50,000 times and yet incredibly increased in power...'

Organon, 6th edition, Section 270 (footnote)

These statements would seem, at first sight, to be contradictory to his view of dilution as a retardant factor. However, this is, in fact, not the case. The clue to unravelling the apparent paradox is given in the following quotation:

'The highest ideal of cure is rapid, gentle and permanent restoration of health, or removal and annihilation of the disease in its whole extent, in the shortest, most reliable, and most harmless way...'

Organon, 6th edition, Section 2

In Hahnemann's view, the most powerful form of medicine is that which cures in accordance with the above principles. Medicines that are harmless, but slower or more incomplete in action, are obviously to be regarded as weaker. Medicines that are excessively strong in action and produce an aggravation of the patient's condition, act against these principles, and are, therefore, also to be regarded as weaker therapeutic agents. The most powerful medicines are swift and complete in therapeutic effect, and unlikely to produce aggravations. Looking at it another way, anything short of optimal is lesser or weaker. Rather like tuning a radio set into a particular station, there is one optimal tuning point, and wavelength points above and below are sub-optimal. By extension of this concept, the LM scale, although more dilute, is considered to be more powerful than the centesimal, in that the potencies produced thereby are more readily attuned to the patient, and, by definition, less likely to induce homoeopathic aggravation. The concept of *power* in Hahnemannian terminology is thus one of *therapeutic power*, and has nothing whatsoever to do with the amplitude of medicinal information or 'energy' contained within the diluent. If anything, it relates to its *qualitative*, rather than its quantitative attributes.

Unfortunately, the consistent inability of homoeopathists in general to comprehend the physicochemical mechanisms involved in potentisation has generated deviant practices, which substitute the whit of the disciple for the profound intuition of the master.

The view of modernists, who believe that quantity and quality are one and the same, has coerced many, with regard to the centesimal potencies, to over-multiply their successions, and to varying degrees. It is not too surprising to learn, therefore, that the Bryonia 6c of one pharmacy exceeds the therapeutic power of the Bryonia 30c of another; and, whilst accepting that this might be explained on the basis of meticulous purity of preparation in the former case, it seems to me more likely that succussion is at the root of the matter. The very existence of the decimal scale, the child of Hahnemann's followers, is also the product of a profession in too much of a hurry and too mean with its alcohol.

The belief that serial dilution enhances the successive development of medicinal effect, rather than attenuates it, has led to a justifiable opposition to our methods, in the face of our inability to explain why. For, a theory based upon an increase in the level of medicinal information dependent upon dilution apparently defies logical conception, whereas one that embraces both dilutional quantitative reduction and qualitative modification does not. Surely it is better said that succussion alone magnifies medicinal energy, and that dilution subdues it. The concept of dilution as a means of attenuation is an easier pill for most to swallow.

However, as will become apparent in the evolution of our discussion, the most palatable medicine is not necessarily the best. We shall discover that potentisation involves the development of two distinct, though physically related, elements within the diluent. One concerns the actual representation of the original solute, and the other relates to *potency* (which, as we shall discuss in Element XX, relates primarily to the range of biological action). Whereas the imprint of the solute upon the diluent is *lessened* by dilution (as one might logically expect), the element of *potency* cannot be *enhanced* unless succussion is preceded by it. Indeed, this matter of presuccussive enhancement by dilution, as we shall propose, is not so illogical and unscientific as, at first, it might seem. Furthermore, we shall see how the vague term 'energy', as it applies to potentised remedies, must be dissected into its various components for it to have any real meaning or significance.

As it would appear, homoeopathists have developed their techniques entirely intuitively, and, in this respect, Hahnemann's intuition would seem to be better than that of his professional progeny. He exhibits a more subtle mastery of the balance between dilution and succussion and its effects, even without an overt knowledge of the processes involved. How much better it would be if we could comprehend the scientific basis for our art, so that those of lesser intuitive capacity could see how they might more elegantly conduct their affairs.

'Water, water everywhere...'

If succussion is the means by which medicinal information is implanted and amplified within the diluent, what is the nature of that *memory?* More pressingly, however, and in gross terms, *where* is it?

There are three basic diluents utilised in homoeopathic pharmacy (fig. 3.1): water, ethanol and lactose (milk sugar). However, whereas it is easy to obtain water that is free of both alcohol and lactose, it is not so simple to exclude water from the latter two. In actual practice, both absolute alcohol and lactose powder always contain a small percentage of water, the amount increasing with the humidity of the preparation area. So, whilst it

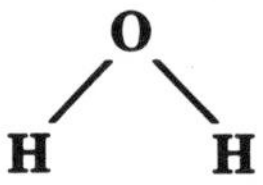

Fig. 3.1. The three diluents of homoeopathy: (1) water (essentially, a 'bifurcate hydroxyl group'); (2) ethanol (with one hydroxyl group); (3) lactose (with eight hydroxyl groups).

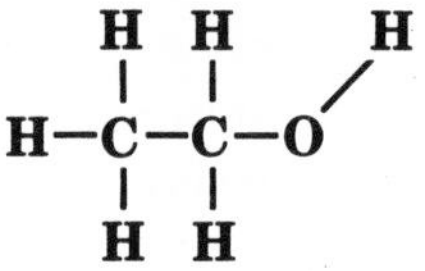

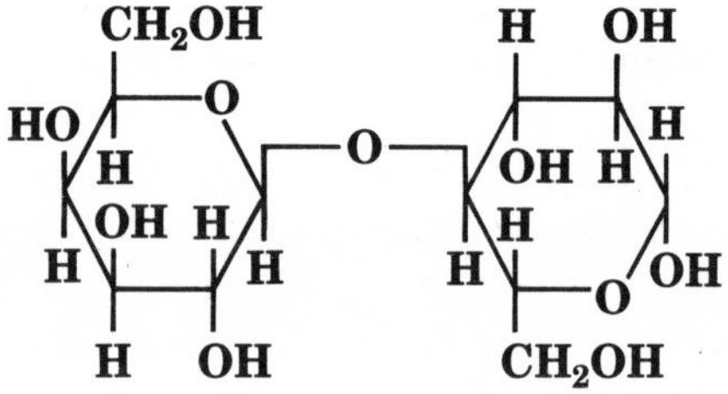

is fairly straightforward to demonstrate that potentisation proceeds in water alone, it is considerably more difficult to establish the same for either pure ethanol or lactose. Nevertheless, as we shall see in due course, all three would seem capable of receiving and retaining what might be termed the *inductive chemical imprint* of other molecules.

In that it has been the focus of much speculative attention on the part of homoeopathic theoreticians, let us first consider water itself. In fact, when we come to look at liquid water in detail, it is more organised than we might assume, and not simply a random mass of hydrogen oxide molecules. In order to unravel the mystery of *water memory* and, therefore, potentisation, we must have sufficient knowledge of its structure, some aspects of which will be more deceptive than pertinent. That water has been so unwilling, thus far, to yield its secrets to the homoeopathist is, perhaps, not too surprising, in that it has also been somewhat unkind to the physical chemist. Potentisation aside, there is still no one theoretical model that explains all the diverse and enigmatic properties of liquid water[13]. In the words of Professor Henry Frank: 'While there has been no dearth of suggestions about what water *might* be like in order to display this or that set of properties, it is only recently ... that it has begun to be possible to draw useful inferences of what water *must* be like in this or that respect. Recent developments do, however, seem to portend real progress towards a comprehensive, self-consistent model of water structure upon which we will be justified in expecting successive approximations to converge.' That water has many mysteries remaining to be accounted for by the physical chemist, must, of necessity, be somewhat reassuring to the homoeopathist, who shrugs his shoulders when asked the nature of water memory. But we shall try do do a little better than that. Conversely, and perhaps unbeknown to him, the physical chemist who builds an 'ultimate' model of water that omits the phenomenon of potentisation will be similarly deficient.

To begin at the beginning, looking at water as H_2O is something of an over-simplification. Both hydrogen and oxygen exist in various isotopic forms; that is to say, their neutrons differ in number (by convention, the *mass number*, which is the total number of protons and neutrons in the given isotope, is expressed as a superscript before the symbol of the element). Those most relevant to the composition of natural waters are: ^1H (the most common form of hydrogen, the nucleus of which consists of a single proton), ^2H (deuterium, often given the symbol D, the nucleus of which consists of one proton and one neutron), ^{16}O (the most common form of oxygen), ^{17}O and ^{18}O. Not surprisingly, the most abundant form of water is $^1H_2^{16}O$, at 997,280 parts per million, followed by $^1H_2^{18}O$ (2000 ppm), $^1H_2^{17}O$ (400 ppm) and $^1H^2H^{16}O$ (320 ppm).

Contrary to popular belief, pure liquid water is an extremely poor conductor of electricity, in that its ability to dissociate into H_3O^+ and OH^- ions is very weak.

Investing in bonds

The *hydrogen bond* may be defined as the weak attraction between an oxygen, nitrogen or fluorine atom in one molecule and a hydrogen atom in an adjacent molecule. In terms of magnitude, it is much stronger than van der Waals' forces, but in general much weaker than covalent or ionic chemical bonds. It is of great importance in understanding the structure and physical properties of both water and ethanol, and is of particular relevance to biological systems, where it is responsible for maintaining the architecture of nucleic acids and proteins. *Base pairing*, the chemical linking of two complementary nitrogenous bases in DNA and in some types of RNA, is effected by hydrogen bonding. In proteins, the bond occurs between the C=O and N–H groups, and stabilises their coiled or pleated *secondary structure*.

The nature of the hydrogen bond is well-exemplified in the case of water. Hydrogen and oxygen atoms bond covalently to produce molecules of water. In the water molecule there are two different types of outer-shell electron pair. Whereas two pairs are shared between oxygen and the hydrogen atoms, in order to bond them together, the remaining two pairs (termed *lone pairs*) belong solely to oxygen (fig. 4.1). The shared pairs, however, are not shared equally. The pull of the oxygen nucleus with its eight protons is stronger than that of hydrogen, which consists only of a single proton. Whilst this pull is partially negated by the shielding effect of the two inner-shell electrons of oxygen, the net result is that the oxygen nucleus attracts shared pairs towards itself and away from the hydrogen nuclei. In essence, each hydrogen atom becomes slightly positively charged ($\delta+$), and the oxygen atom becomes slightly negatively charged ($\delta-$). Molecules that exhibit an uneven spread of charge are termed *polar molecules*, of which water is one example.

The more positive end of a water molecule attracts the more negative end of another. In other words, each hydrogen atom of the water molecule is capable of attracting the oxygen atom of an adjacent water molecule (fig. 4.1). The hydrogen bond thus formed may be simply considered as an electrostatic force of attraction between oppositely charged poles of water molecules. However, and more precisely, the slightly positively charged hydrogen atom is actually attracted to a single lone pair of oxygen electrons of the neighbouring molecule. Since this lone pair is now partially influenced by the hydrogen atom, it is stated that the hydrogen bond so formed is to be regarded as being partly covalent in nature.

The tendency of water molecules to form hydrogen bonds leads to the production of polymeric aggregates within the liquid phase, termed *clusters*. Ethanol, which has many physical properties similar to those of water, though commanding a higher price, also forms polymers by means of hydrogen bonding.

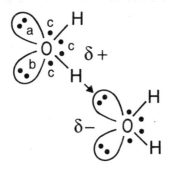

Fig. 4.1 Water molecules and the hydrogen bond. With regard to each molecule, note the two lone pairs of electrons (a and b). The electrons (c) shared between oxygen and hydrogen are more strongly attracted to oxygen. The hydrogen bond is indicated by an arrow.

Crystal gazing for fun and profit

As I have stated, the structure of liquid water is still controversial. X-ray scattering studies, however, have confirmed the existence of short-range, ordered, 'ice-like' regions (polymeric clusters) which are continually disintegrating and re-forming. This high degree of structure, dependent upon hydrogen bonding, accounts for some of the more unusual properties of water. Water's *fixed points* of 0°C and 100°C, for example, are particularly high. In contrast, hydrogen sulphide (H_2S), which does not form hydrogen bonds, freezes at minus 83°C and boils at minus 62°C! The ordering of the liquid phase of water is sufficient to render the density of water at about 0°C higher than that of the relatively open-structured ice; hence the phenomenon of ice floating on water. In fact, the maximum density occurs at 3.98°C.

The fact that liquid water shows a such high degree of organisation or pattern, together with the necessity to find some ordered structure in water to carry the individual *inductive chemical imprints* of homoeopathic remedies, has placed much emphasis on its ability to form polymeric clusters; although, as we shall see, such faith in what appears to be obvious may be somewhat misguided. Nature, like 'the economy', is apparently more insidious in its physics!

Perhaps the most popular model of liquid water is that of Frank and Wen[19], where polymeric clusters form irregular crystalloid (ordered) globules, between which are situated free water molecules, unassociated by hydrogen bonding (fig. 5.1). It would be quite natural to assume that these clusters might well be our homoeopathic messengers. We might envisage that, during succussion, each cluster is able to adopt an individual conformation characteristic of an original substance (solute), thus to form an encoded message of biological significance. Furthermore, with each successive phase of potentisation, we might expect further aggregation of

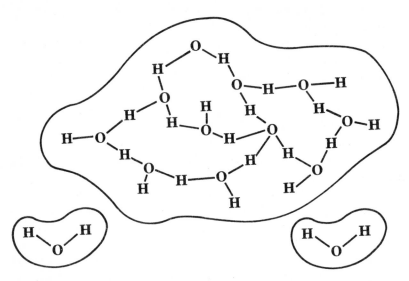

Fig. 5.1 A schematic diagram of a three-dimensional polymeric water cluster. Two free water molecules are beside it.

water molecules by means of hydrogen bonding, so that each cluster enlarges whilst maintaining its unique crystalloid architecture. Simple and elegant though these propositions may seem, are they in fact reasonable?

In the first place, studies carried out by Némethy and Scheraga[19] have shown that the ability of water to form clusters is strongly dependent upon its temperature, to which it is inversely related. This in itself is, perhaps, not surprising, for without such a propensity for the reduction of hydrogen bonding with increased thermal energy, we would be unable to make water boil and enter its gaseous phase (steam). They have assessed that the average cluster size ranges from 91 to 25 molecules of water over the temperature range from 0°C to 70°C, the average cluster size at 20°C (approximately the temperature at which most homoeopathic remedies are prepared) being 57 molecules. In view of the constraints of hydrogen bonding, these figures would hardly suggest a crystalloid mechanism capable of the individual representation of a large number of possible solutes. Admittedly, however, these studies were carried out on ordinary water, and not that subjected to homoeopathic potentisation technique. There still remains the possibility, therefore, that larger clusters, with greater representational capacity, might be formed during succussion. However, spectroscopic studies on liquid potencies have failed to demonstrate the expected increase in hydrogen bond activity (personal communication). Furthermore, any increase in cluster size as a result of succussion would imply that both the boiling and freezing points of the diluent would be raised; a matter which, to my knowledge, has never been verified.

Beyond these facts, there is yet one other problem. The life of each hydrogen bond in water, as estimated by Frank and Wen, is in the order of 10^{-11} to 10^{-10} of a second. The life expectancy of each cluster in ordinary water is, therefore, extremely short. In the *flickering cluster model* of these authors, the clusters are constantly forming, disintegrating and re-forming at new sites. As the hydrogen bonds disappear in one area, they reappear, so to speak, to form new clusters from free (unbonded) water molecules elsewhere. In this way, the number of hydrogen bonds per unit of volume, at a given temperature and atmospheric pressure, remains more or less constant, and the viscosity of the water does not change to any appreciable degree.

Theories of potentisation based on the conventional model of ordinary water are thus fraught with difficulties. Not only are the cluster sizes insufficient to represent solute information, their mean size is further reduced by increases in temperature. Furthermore, these clusters do not remain in cohesive existence for more than a brief moment in time. Neither is there any spectroscopic or thermal evidence of any increased density of hydrogen bonding in the case of succussed liquid potencies.

Collecting shells as a hobby

Concepts of potentisation that suggest changes in diluent architecture as a basis for the phenomenon may be termed *geometrical hypotheses* (or *theories*). In Element V we considered and essentially rejected one such version.

Before proceeding to investigate other hypotheses, it is pertinent to consider which aspects of the solute the diluent might represent. Here, we have but two major alternatives: the *electromagnetic characteristics* of the solute molecules (including frequencies dependent upon chemical bond vibrations), and their *molecular shapes* (or geometries). Initially, however, we shall concern ourselves with concepts relating to the latter, which are themselves geometrical hypotheses with regard to the diluent. In this respect, we must discuss *hydration shells*[12].

Hydration shells are formed by the close electrostatic association of water molecules with *ions* or the poles of other *polar molecules*. The majority of substances subjected to potentisation are comprised of such ions or polar molecules. As you will recall, the water molecule has an electrically negative oxygen pole and two electrically positive hydrogen poles. In the case of a *cation* (a positively charged ion), such as Na^+, the negative (oxygen) poles of the water molecules are attracted towards it, so that their long axes radiate outwards, with their positive (hydrogen) poles being situated on the periphery (fig. 6.1). In the case of an *anion* (a negatively charged ion), such as Cl^-, the radiation is similar, but the polarity of attraction is reversed, with the oxygen atoms being positioned on the periphery. In this way, ions become engulfed by a closely associated structure composed of a single layer of water molecules, termed the *primary hydration shell* (or *primary solvent sheath*). Between the primary hydration shell and the bulk water is a zone of compromise orientation of water molecules, termed the *secondary hydration shell*. You will be able to imagine a similar association of water molecules with the positive and negative poles of any polar molecule. In this

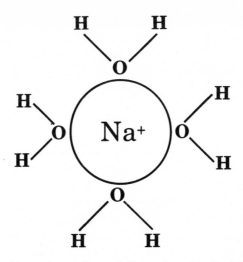

Fig. 6.1 Water molecules forming an hydration shell around a positive ion (sodium).

manner, the hydration shell (more importantly, its primary component) produces a negative shape, rather like a plaster cast, of the engulfed ion or molecular pole.

In various hypotheses of potentisation based upon this notion, it is envisaged that, during dilution, the shell splits open to release the engulfed particle (ion or molecule); the fragments of the hydration cast either reforming into a complete cast, or collapsing down to produce a positive representation of the original particulate shape (though obviously different in size).

The main weakness of such hypotheses of potentisation is apparent when we re-examine the orientation of the water molecules of the primary hydration shell. Like poles of the water molecules always point towards each other in the presence of the charged particle. As soon as the particle is released by dilution, the water molecules so orientated will be pushed apart by electrostatic repulsion, and thus cannot re-form the shell. Perhaps the fragments might persist within the diluent as pieces of a 'jig-saw puzzle' capable of reassembly at a biological receptor? Their persistence alone would be something of a miracle in the face of vigorous succussion, which would tend to destroy their unique orientation. Beyond that, primary hydration shells formed in relation to most monovalent, monoatomic ions consist of only four molecules of water. What possible information could be extracted from a fragment of such a shell consisting of one or two molecules only?

Before we leave the topic of geometrical representation, one further hypothesis is worthy of mention. Although it does not seem to be concerned with the memory of solute molecular shape, it does appear to relate to the representation of solute electromagnetic properties. Berezin[5] was apparently inspired by the well-known Benveniste[9] experiments to compose this model, which is based upon the isotopic diversity of water: '... some positional correlations of stable isotope (H, D, ^{16}O, ^{17}O and ^{18}O) might work as 'templates' of the originally dissolved molecules. These isotopic correlations are equivalent to the choice of a particular isotopic pattern out of the highly degenerate manyfold (manifold) of potentially available patterns. This pattern is further reproduced at the next dilution level by some sort of 'locking-in' mechanism.' The problem with this hypothesis is that it makes no mention of the basis for increased biological reactivity with serial succussion. However, to give the author his due, he does make the following conclusive comments: 'This explanation does not dismiss the possibility of other alternative explanations. Moreover, it could turn out to be complementary to them.'

Personally, I am suspicious of all essentially geometrical hypotheses of potentisation, in that they are excessively simplistic concepts of what must be a remarkably accurate and exceedingly complex phenomenon, which not only relates to water and alcohol, but also to solids, such as lactose, and probably many other substances.

Group behaviour in goldfish bowls

Theories (or hypotheses, if you prefer) concerning the mechanism of potentisation may be conveniently classified into three groups: *geometrical* (discussed previously), *dynamic field* (described below), and *submolecular* (considered later). Inevitably, of course, there is some overlap. For example, in one sense, the isotopic hypothesis outlined previously is *submolecular*, in that it finds its basis in nuclear mass variation. However, since its main premise implies a static rearrangement of diluent architecture, it is better classified as *geometrical*. Despite its limitations, the given classification forms a sensible basis for understanding the many and varied propositions that have been made by various authors.

Since *dynamic field theories* are much in vogue, it is appropriate to discuss their general principles next. However, before doing so, we should identify and define the various components of a *solute*. Firstly, we have the *intended solute*; that is to say, the deliberately added pharmaceutical molecules. Secondly, there is the *aerogenous solute*, consisting of the dissolved gases of the air. Thirdly, there is the *contaminant solute*, composed of impurities contained within the diluent, and substances (most importantly, sodium and hydroxyl ions) leached from the walls of the glass vessel. Of the *non-aerogenous solute* (intended plus contaminant), only the intended component is usually completely removed by serial dilution.

The main propositions of the dynamic field theories may be enumerated thus:

(1) That the solute produces an individually characteristic vibrating electromagnetic field, with a unique frequency related to its components and their relative molecular presence.

(2) That various components of the diluent (viz. water clusters or hydrogen bonds) or of the aerogenous solute (viz. oxygen, nitrogen

or carbon dioxide molecules) become attuned to this frequency, and collectively 'resonate' (sympathetically vibrate) in accord with it.

(3) That the vibrations of the characteristic electromagnetic field and the resonantly vibrating components of the diluent or aerogenous solute maintain each other mutually, so that such vibrations persist even after the removal of the intended solute by serial dilution.

Let us now consider in further detail the various 'resonant' components that have been the subject of homoeopathic theorisation.

Perhaps, one of the simplest versions of dynamic field theory concerns *hydrogen bonding*. It has been suggested that the normal formation and destruction of such bonds adopts a collective rhythmicity throughout the diluent in response to the vibration of the electromagnetic field of the solute.

Alternative theories maintain that the *aerogenous solute is* the most appropriate resonant component. More precisely, water molecules are known to form structures, termed *clathrate hydrates*[13], which consist of hydrogen-bonded spheroidal, crystalloid (organised) aggregates, with central cavities containing non-polar, non-ionic (uncharged) molecules of the solute. Within these central voids, the so-called *guest molecules* (in this case, the captured gas molecules) are allowed to 'rattle around', and exhibit an oscillatory motion. Collectively, it is proposed, the captured aerogenous molecules exhibit a vibratory frequency characteristic of the solute.

A third type of theory proposes the induction of specific arrangements within water clusters as the seat of resonant harmony. The idea is that water molecules are segregated into two different groups (or phases), which are uniformly distributed throughout the vial. One group consists of water clusters in which the constituent molecules exhibit specific orientations of their electrical poles in accord with the electromagnetic field of the solute. The other group consists of clusters and free water molecules responding to the normal thermodynamic effects associated with water; that is to say, the maintenance of the expected density of hydrogen bonding according to temperature, and the apparently random destruction and generation of clusters. The thermodynamic effect of cluster-size reduction with increasing temperature is thus minimised with respect to the electromagnetically orientated group. It is postulated that, even after removal of the intended solute by serial dilution, the mutual support of the characteristic electromagnetic field and the orientated cluster molecules is capable of maintaining their reciprocal integrity in the face of the cyclical destruction and formation of linking hydrogen bonds. It is thus conjectured that, unlike the thermodynamically sensitive group of clusters, which are continually disrupted by hydrogen bond dissolution, the ordered clusters maintain their structure by continual re-formation of hydrogen bonds at the same sites.

Another form of theory proposes that the electromagnetic field of the solute induces the production of 'resonating' stable *helical* polymeric clusters within the diluent, with five water molecules per turn of the helix. It is thought that, whilst they can be broken by succussion, the fragments subsequently rejoin with each other, or attract free water molecules to produce new helical seedlings, and that such structures are persistent even after removal of the intended solute. These helical ropes or coils may be regarded as spiral preferential electrical conductive paths, and as such have solenoid-like properties, with the induction of internal magnetic fields. However, the 'current' passing along through these coils is conceived to be *protonic* rather than electronic. That is to say, by means of what is termed a *soliton mechanism*, protons (hydrogen nuclei) 'hop' across the hydrogen bond bridges linking the water molecules. Such a mechanism not only produces what amounts to a current of positive electricity, it also contributes to the preservation and stability of the helical polymers. Interestingly enough, ethanol is also capable of forming helical polymers, and thus may be included in these concepts. As with other theories (described above) that maintain the persistence of organised clusters, the thermodynamic balance of the diluent must be maintained by the presence of clusters and free molecules not so electromagnetically constrained.

For further elucidation of this complex subject of dynamic fields, the reader is advised to refer to the various papers (quoted in the bibliography) by Antonchenko and Ilyin[1], Del Giudice[10], Popp[20], Resch and Gutmann[22], and Smith[27]; from which the above ideas have been modified and predigested, so as to render them (hopefully) fit for the consumption of normal mortals.

ELEMENT VIII

Cacohydrophonics

Were there some truth in the *dynamic field* concept of potentisation, one might expect to find some scientific physical corroboration of the existence of 'resonating' electromagnetic fields in liquid potencies.

In fact, some evidence has been forthcoming from various workers using low-frequency spectroscopy (spectrometry). Ludwig (quoted by Smith[28]), for example, found the principal frequency for Phosphorus 6x (D6) to be 300Hz, and that of Arnica 1000x (D1000) to be 9.725kHz. Endler[11] concludes, however, that whilst specific rhythmic vibration patterns do exist in both water and alcohol, such patterns do change according to the manner in which they have been treated; for example, from potency to potency (quoting Klima, Kokoschinegg, and Rasche).

It would seem, therefore, that these observations lead to the inevitable conclusion that the recorded frequencies are more likely a function of serial succussion. That is to say, they correspond to the level of potency, rather than to any specific molecular electromagnetic frequency of the solute which might characterise it individually.

Another (but lesser) problem, which need only concern the protagonists of the aerogenous vibratory system, is that gas molecules are insufficiently rigid to generate mechanical vibrations in the kHz region necessary to support like electromagnetic frequencies. In an attempt to overcome this theoretical problem, there has been suggested a collective inter-relationship between all the dissolved gas molecules by energetic exchange (e.g. electron-photon-coupling), thus enabling them to indulge in 'resonance' with the higher frequency fields. However, since, as we shall see in Element XI, certain spectroscopic studies have indicated distinct structural changes in the diluent consequent upon potentisation, it would seem unlikely that the aerogenous solute plays anything other than a minor (and perhaps unessential) contributory role in the homoeopathic process.

Fortuitously, the aerogenous theory is only one of several concerning dynamic fields. Nevertheless, we still must contend with the apparently disappointing conclusion that the implanted frequencies within the diluent are more representative of potency than of solute molecular characteristics. What we should ask ourselves is whether such a result might have been predictable? Indeed, when we come to analyse the vibrations of polyatomic molecules in general[17,30] we are compelled to appreciate the virtual impossibility of specific representation in terms of a simple and specific frequency; and to this point we shall turn next.

It is a fact that everything in the Universe is in a state of continual motion, variously characterised and categorised as translatory, orbital, rotatory, gyratory, oscillatory, or vibratory. Indeed, polyatomic molecules exhibit a complex vibrational motion associated with the dynamics of their chemical bonds. Each of these bonds is capable of undergoing certain transformations, in the form of shortening, lengthening and bending. As a result, in the case of a non-linear (angulated) triatomic molecule y-x-y (such as SO_2, sulphur dioxide), three *vibrational modes* are distinguishable (fig. 8.1):

(1) Symmetric stretching, where the bonds y-x and x-y lengthen together.
(2) Symmetric bending, where the bonds y-x and x-y bend so as to produce deformation of the bond angle y-x-y.
(3) Antisymmetric stretching, where y-x lengthens and x-y shortens (or vice versa).

Vibrational modes are investigated by both infrared and Raman spectroscopy. The vibrational dynamics of each bond depend fundamentally upon the nature of the constituent atoms (in the above case, x and y), and each vibrational mode is defined in terms of a characteristic frequency. However, for the purists (and only for them), it should be mentioned that, in some situations, two vibrational modes may *couple*, so as to produce two very similar frequencies, expressing contributions from both. The two stretching modes, nominally C–D and C≡N stretches, of the linear molecule DCN constitute an example, where, what is conceptualised as the

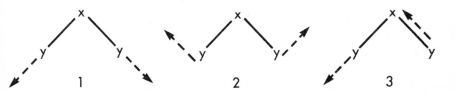

Fig. 8.1 The three vibrational modes of a non-linear triatomic molecule: (1) symmetric stretching; (2) symmetric bending; (3) antisymmetric stretching.

spectroscopic C–D band, in fact possesses a 34% contribution from C≡N stretching.

As the triatomic molecule changes from one mode of vibration to the next, so its characteristic frequency changes. Hence, even such a simple molecule exhibits three different fundamental frequencies. By convention, however, vibrational modes (v_n) are quantified in terms of *wave numbers*, the units of which are cm^{-1}(although these are often loosely referred to as 'vibrational frequencies'). In fact, these are directly proportional to the actual frequencies in Hz, since

$$v_n (cm^{-1}) = f(Hz)/c,$$

where f is the actual frequency and c is the velocity of light *in vacuo* (cm/s^{-1}).

In practice, stretching vibrations are at higher frequencies than bending frequencies involving similar atoms. The values for the molecule O–S–O (SO_2), for example, are:

v_1: symmetric S–O stretch $1148cm^{-1}$
v_2: O–S–O deformation $521cm^{-1}$
v_3: antisymmetric S–O stretch $1349cm^{-1}$

When we examine more complex molecules, we find the number of possible vibrational modes to be even larger; each mode, of course, being defined in terms of a characteristic wave number (vibrational frequency). In this respect, two examples will suffice: the molecule $POCl_3$, and the ion $PtCl_4^{2-}$, each composed of five atoms.

The vibrational modes and frequencies (wave numbers) of $POCl_3$ are listed as follows:

v_1 P=O stretch $1290cm^{-1}$
v_2: symmetric P-Cl stretch $486cm^{-1}$
v_3: symmetric deformation $267cm^{-1}$
v_4: degenerate P-Cl stretch $581cm^{-1}$
v_5: deformations $337cm^{-1}$
v_6: $193cm^{-1}$

For $PtCl_4^{2-}$ the vibrational modes and their characteristic frequencies (wave numbers) are:

v_1: symmetric Pt-Cl stretch $332cm^{-1}$
v_2: antisymmetric Pt-CI stretch $314cm^{-1}$
v_3: in-plane deformation $170cm^{-1}$

v_4: out-of-plane deformation $93cm^{-1}$
[v_5: out-of-plane deformation – inactive]
v_6: Pt-Cl stretch $320cm^{-1}$
v_7: in-plane deformation $183cm^{-1}$

It should now be quite obvious that, in terms of bond vibration, a polyatomic molecule is not represented by a single frequency, but rather by a *set of characteristic frequencies*. In addition to these fundamental frequencies, it is worthy of mention that others may be elicited by further energisation of the molecule. In spectroscopic terms, these are referred to as *overtone and combination bands*, and these should be added to the set of characteristic frequencies in order to define it more precisely.

Our main interest, of course, is the effect of characteristic bond vibrations on the induced magnetic field surrounding the molecule. Whereas spectroscopy analyses these vibrational characteristics in an individual and selective manner, and dissects them from the totality of vibrational motion, the reality is somewhat different. In actuality, different parts of a complex molecule manifest different vibrational modes at the same time. At any particular instant, therefore, several or many different vibrational frequencies will be involved in the induction of an encircling magnetic field; and those modes and frequencies will change from instant to instant. Hence, the frequency of the magnetic field, which may be regarded as an average of those modal frequencies, will also change in the same manner, and thus will never be constant. In fact, the vibrational modal transformations within a molecule appear to occur quite randomly, unless influenced by specific forms of energy, such as that provided by spectroscopic examination.

In order to conceptualise the situation, imagine a polar polyatomic molecule as an articulated, one-legged, wooden marionette (string puppet), with the joints representing the chemical bonds, the head acting as the positive electrical pole, and the foot acting as the negative. As an electrical pole moves or vibrates, so a magnetic field is induced with the same vibrational frequency. Thus, as the marionette is jiggled vigorously by its strings, so the head and the foot generate such fields. However, neither end of the marionette moves with a frequency that is of any apparent consistency and regularity. The movements are, in a sense, governed by the summation of all the motions of the joints and wooden members situated between head and foot. Only by studying these actions in slow-motion will it become evident that the apparent irregularity of motion is composed of brief bursts of distinct and different frequencies, following each other with great rapidity;

this occurring in a quantised manner, with one frequency switching to the next without any intermediate vibrational phase.

The situation worsens when we pass from a consideration of individual molecules of solute to the greater issue of their collective induction of a magnetic *dynamic field*. It is not unreasonable to suggest that even chemically identical molecules of the solute do not vibrate in unison. This point should be self-evident from my comment on the random nature of vibrational modal transformations within each molecule. Whereas it is conceivable that, at a particular instant, certain molecules of solute, randomly distributed throughout the solution, might be in phase, these will be out of phase with the remainder, and vice versa.

Taking all these various facets into consideration, it is very difficult to see how the induced magnetic field of the solute, considered in its entirety, can have any recognisable form that is ascribable to the individual structure of the molecules that have induced it. So, whilst we may glibly discuss dynamic fields and their relationship to the diluent, what use are such cacophonic and unploughed entities that do not represent what we feel they should?

ELEMENT IX

Alcohol and the commune

At this juncture, let us divert our attention to the consideration of a few relevant details of the properties of the second major diluent in homoeopathy, viz. *ethanol*.

Ethanol, of course, is an excellent solvent from our point of view, not only with regard to many organic materials, but also with respect to inorganic salts, such as sodium chloride. Hence its use in the preparation of mother tinctures, and its value in averting the precipitation of solute in the early stages of serial dilution.

One of the major roles of ethanol, as many will be aware, is to act as a preservative against fungal and bacterial growth. Whereas serial potentisation may be satisfactorily carried out with relatively weak ethanol-water as the diluent (say, 14%), except in the earliest stages, any liquid potency intended for storage (e.g. 30c, 200c) ideally should be prepared with 90–95% ethanol-water. This apparently dull truth may, however, be of some further significance. It has been suggested, in fact, that one reason for the wide popularity of the standard potencies (such as 6c, 12c, 30c, 200c and 1M), rather than intermediate alternatives (e.g. 5c, 28c, 180c and 910c), is that they represent points of spontaneous 'quantum leap' in energy, and, therefore, in biological strength of action; implying that there is little therapeutic advantage to be gained by prescribing other betwixt and between potencies. Perhaps any such leap is due, in reality, to the change in alcohol strength for the dispensed potency. Although, as we shall see, ethanol is similar in many ways to water, there are, nevertheless, some notable differences beyond its ability to intoxicate. It may well be that ethanol is more readily potentised than water because of its lower surface tension and its different ability to form polymers; both matters to be discussed subsequently. Bearing in mind that the French writers often favour what we (as British and American homoeopathists) might consider as intermediate potencies (such as 5c, 9c and 14c), it might be true that the higher alcoholic strength of the dispensed potency is of greater significance than might be generally appreciated, and that spontaneous 'quantum leaps' at various points, specifically related to certain numbered stages of serial dilution, might be a mere figment of the homoeopathic imagination. Indeed, it may be the case that such leaps in strength might occur at any stage of potentisation, should there be an abrupt increase in the alcoholic strength of the diluent; and thus are more contrived than spontaneous, and not associated with any particular potency. It would certainly seem that a liquid potency containing ethanol is better than one where the diluent is water alone, in that it retains its therapeutic potential for a considerably longer period.

One particular virtue of ethanol is its action in lowering surface tension. In this way, succussion more readily energises and mobilises the molecules of the liquid potency; for less energy is then required to fracture surface films, which not only exist at the top of the solution, but also are generated within by the cavitation (bubbles) produced by vigorous shaking. This, perhaps, is one reason why potentisation proceeds more readily in the presence of ethanol.

Ethanol, rather like water, has a relatively high boiling point: approximately 78°C. This is partly related to its propensity to form hydrogen bonds and thus polymers. However, this propensity differs from that of water, which, as we have seen, can form complex three-dimensional clusters and clathrates. In the case of ethanol, such three-dimensional arrays cannot be formed, and only linear or cyclic polymers exist. In this way, ethanol is not so highly structured as water, which puts yet another nail in the coffin of various geometrical theories of potentisation. Neither does this tend to support a dynamic field theory that relies on complex polymers to maintain a specific and characteristic electromagnetic field; since, if such were true, water should be more effectively potentised and manifest greater prolongation of potency than ethanol. This, apparently, is not the case.

Nevertheless, in terms of the *submolecular theories* of potentisation, with which we have yet to deal, such a lesser complexity of polymeric architecture is advantageous. With regard to these theories, as we shall discover, one of the proposed roles of succussion is to fracture the hydrogen bonds of the diluent molecules, so as to free them for collision with each other or with molecules of solute. Since ethanol has a lesser proclivity to form hydrogen bonds than water, it follows that less energy of succussion is required to disrupt its polymeric forms, and that more energy can be devoted to the translatory motion of the molecules, and hence collision.

ELEMENT X

Finding fruit in barren fields

Having had a brief respite from the *dynamic field theories* of potentisation, we shall now return to them to see what we might salvage of value.

Material to these theories is the belief that the diluent (or the aerogenous solute), at least partially, remains in a state of energisation greater than its 'ground state', even after the intended solute has been removed. This extra energy, of course, must be supplied by the conversion of the crude mechanical energy of succussion. To these general points, one can offer no sensible objection .

However, as we have seen in Element VIII, the electromagnetic field generated by the solute does not portray its molecular composition in terms of any specific frequency. Indeed, it is so garbled, that it is unlikely even to represent this composition in terms of a variety of frequencies. However, we are still faced with the fact that curious resonant frequencies can be elicited from liquid potencies, and these, we have suggested, are expressive of the level of potency, rather than molecular structure; that is to say, they would appear to be dependent upon the summation of the serial mechanical energisation of the vial contents. Smith[28], for example, states that one worker's measurements over a range of potencies of Sulphur covered the whole of the audio frequency region, with frequencies specified to 0.01Hz.

It follows, therefore, that the molecules of the diluent (or, less likely, those of the aerogenous solute) must behave in some cooperative fashion to produce such distinct potency-related frequencies. So, in this limited respect, there must exist a dynamic electromagnetic field associated with these frequencies, which must have a mutually supportive inter-relationship with the molecules of the diluent (now ignoring, for convenience, the less likely cooperative action of the aerogenous solute). The question, then, is how can the diluent molecules manifest such an organised behaviour in terms of their 'recognised' properties?

In terms of orthodox physicochemical knowledge, the persistence of a higher energetic state of the diluent after succussion is untenable, whether the intended solute is present or rendered absent by serial dilution. This much is deducible from the *known* properties of molecules in general, which should return quite rapidly to their previous energetic ground state after each episode of mechanical energisation (succussion), with the production of dispersible heat (since external forces between the molecules, such as friction and electrostatic attraction, oppose their acquired kinetic inertia). Therefore, the presence of a *persistent* dynamic electromagnetic field, with a supportive molecular structure, should not exist. However, this position is in conflict with the experimental facts. So how do we circumvent this particular problem?

As it transpires, the principal difference between the orthodox and the homoeopathic point of view is the speed of events. Orthodoxy dictates a swift return (seconds or minutes) to the ground energetic state following succussion, and homoeopathy a slow return (weeks or years, according to the composition of the diluent).

It is true, however, that orthodoxy accepts the existence of so-called *metastable states* under certain circumstances. Essentially, these are prolonged but unstable higher states of energisation, which either slowly and spontaneously return to the ground state, or do so rapidly when disturbed. A form of luminescence known as *phosphorescence* is an example, where metastable electronic excitation exhibits a slow decay. Supercooled water, which is liquid below 0°C, is also in a metastable state; but rapidly returns to its ground energetic state by freezing, when a grain of dust or ice is introduced. The problem is that non-homoeopaths have not appreciated that metastability can also exist in mechanically agitated solutions and their serially diluted and energised derivatives. Obviously, the metastability of liquid potencies is more akin to phosphorescence in terms of rate of decay, but, as some would hold, only in that respect; for, as they maintain, succussion is of insufficient force to result in direct electronic excitation.

If not electronic, what is the physical foundation for homoeopathic metastability? Is it, perhaps, more structurally akin to supercooled water, and only similar to phosphorescence in its persistence? This would certainly seem to be the view of some dynamic field theorists (though the issue is sometimes clouded by involving the resonance of the aerogenous solute in the phenomenon as a contributory element). Gutmann and Resch[22] talk of *supermolecular system organisation*, and Del Giudice[10] refers to *superradiance*. These, as it happens, turn out to be different names for the same thing. The idea is that we cannot deduce from the known physical properties of individual molecules how they will behave collectively. Whereas an individual molecule of the diluent subjected to a brief application of mechanical energy will rapidly return to its ground state, a collection of molecules may not. It is explained that Nature is more inclined towards order rather than disorder. Whilst the ground state is less energetic than the mechanically excited state, the individual molecules of the diluent at that level behave incoherently; that is to say, they vibrate in a disorderly manner (disordered energy). It is inferred that Nature prefers the elegance (or coherence) of the molecules vibrating harmoniously (ordered energy); even at the cost of maintaining a higher state of excitation.

With regard to these matters, Gutmann and Resch, who are obviously opposed to reductionism, state: 'All attempts in modern science to gain an understanding of the macroscopic properties of a given system start at the properties of its widely separated molecules. This reductionistic approach is, however, based on a philosophical attitude which ignores the fundamental requirements of quantum mechanics, according to which molecules are never isolated, but rather united within the continuous charge density pattern extending throughout the Universe.' At first sight, this appears to be a somewhat esoteric evasion, that substitutes a new natural philosophy for a current lack of understanding of the properties of matter. It could be argued, in fact, that our knowledge of atoms and molecules is too limited at present to account for the cooperative behaviour under consideration, viz. that associated with potentisation. However, I am inclined to think that their statement is to be regarded as rather more profound than at first it might seem. Whether wittingly or unwittingly, the authors have described a fundamental *uncertainty principle* of great significance, which may be formulated thus: that the totality of the properties of individual molecules, as deduced from experimental observation, can never be used to deduce or predict their observable collective behaviour under *all* physical conditions. This we may term the *collective uncertainty principle*.

In fact, built into our modern notions of the nature of the atom and atomic phenomena is an unavoidable set of principles of *uncertainty*.

The idea of *wave-particle duality* illustrates this point. This is the concept that waves carrying energy may have a corpuscular (particulate) aspect, and that particles may have a wave aspect. Which of the two models is more appropriate depends upon the properties the model is seeking to explain. For example, electromagnetic waves need to be conceptualised as particles, termed *photons,* in order to explain the photoelectric effect, whilst electrons (which are normally visualised as being particulate) need to be thought of as *de Broglie waves* in electron diffraction. So, both rays of light and electrons may be viewed as what might be termed *wave-particles*. Here, the uncertainty is whether, under any new set of physical circumstances, the wave-particle will behave as either a wave or a particle, and this can only be determined by experiment.

Another facet of uncertainty concerns the position of a given electron in relation to the atomic nucleus at any particular moment, which can never be *predicted* exactly, and must be expressed in terms of probability. This is because Newton's laws of motion, though applicable to cannon-balls, do not apply to electrons.

A final example is the *Heisenberg uncertainty principle*. This essentially states that the simultaneous measurement of position and momentum of a particle cannot produce accurate results, since the act of observing the system (by bouncing a photon of electromagnetic radiation off the particle) interferes with it in an unpredictable way. This principle is of importance at the atomic and subatomic level, and a similar uncertainty exists with regard to the simultaneous measurement of time and energy.

These various principles of uncertainty (and there are more) place *obligatory* constraints on our experimental cognizance of matter and energy, leaving the areas of doubt to be debated by philosophers and metaphysicists. The *collective uncertainty principle* indicates that there are limits placed on the information we may gain about a particular substance (e.g. water) by experimentation upon a single isolated system (e.g. pure water). In order to approximate to an overall knowledge of a substance, we must also observe, without prejudice, how it behaves in a number of different collective situations (e.g. in the earlier and later stages of potentisation).

The problem is rather like that of the proverbial 'chicken and egg' (forgetting about which came first!). Does the fertilised egg contain an immensely complex code which determines the function and position of every cell in the chicken; or do those cells, as they are produced, develop new properties of organisation which are not contained in the codes of the egg? If Del Giudice, Gutmann and Resch are correct in their ideas of 'superradiance' or 'supermolecular system organisation', as they might well be, then the secret of life is not to be found in the egg alone.

There is, however, one more philosophical point to be unravelled. How can we be sure that the molecule or the egg does not contain the programme that we ascribe to supermolecular system organisation (superradiance), bearing in mind the constraints of the principles of uncertainty? Perhaps they are there, but our observation of them is 'disallowed'. This dilemma, unfortunately, is insoluble in terms of our current understanding of the Universe. All we can say is that new properties *become apparent* when molecules or cells form larger groups. The contemplation of the unfathomable is best left to the dinner party.

We now have an organised group of diluent molecules with a mutually supportive electromagnetic field vibrating in harmony. This dynamic field is identifiable in terms of a particular frequency, depending on how much serial mechanical energy has been applied. So, where is the 'model' of the solute held?

Regrettably, the dynamic field concept of potentisation does not supply the answer. As we have seen in Element VIII, it fails to explain how the diluent is implanted with a coherent imprint of the solute. It does, however, give us some insight into the way information concerning level of potency is stored (it fails, nevertheless, to explain how the diluent molecules communicate with each other to form an harmonious group; this being a matter for further discussion).

In order to understand how a true (coherent) inductive chemical imprint might be produced, we must now turn away from the dynamic field concept and look into the *submolecular theories* of potentisation.

However, before proceeding, let us consider the old hermetic axiom 'As above, so below', often quoted, and implying that the microcosm is an image of the macrocosm, and vice versa. The revelations that the laws that govern the motion of the planets do not apply to the electrons orbiting around a nucleus, and those of supermolecular system organisation (superradiance) both finally lay to rest this ancient adage.

ELEMENT XI

Galileo as a health hazard

In order to look further into possible theories of potentisation, we must digress slightly and review some more of the results that have been obtained by physicochemical experimentation.

Since homoeopathic remedies are powerful and largely reliable therapeutic agents, it would be somewhat surprising if we could not find observable and measurable changes in liquid potencies, even at the *infinitesimal* levels of serial potentisation, where no molecules of the intended solute remain. Indeed, comment has already been made with regard to the curious potency-related frequencies elicited by some workers.

Unfortunately, as we have come to realise, the acceptance or rejection of experimental results is not only dependent on their technical and statistical validity, but also upon the prejudices of the scientific world[23]. Although the truth of homoeopathic therapeutics has been plainly demonstrated in certain respects by properly controlled clinical trials, there are still those who believe, quite illogically (and, therefore, emotively), that homoeopathy is the prescription of placebos. I have often illustrated the point by stating that the important theoretical work of Albert Einstein with regard to relativity, were it currently unknown, and being the unorthodox and speculative text of a mere clerk, would not be published in any 'respectable' scientific journal; let alone would it command much attention. Who knows what they would think of Galileo, dropping cannon-balls, pizzas or whatever from the Leaning Tower of Pisa, and playing with chandeliers? Perhaps if something were to fall on the head of a member of the establishment, he might gain some recognition, but then only in the popular tabloid press! More important than results, apparently, is belonging to the right club, and, as Benveniste[9] discovered to his cost, not breaking its rules (Galileo's favourite past-time). Fame, it would seem, is as metastable as supercooled water, and readily precipitates into infamy.

Hence, even the most lax of scientific observations and the most avant-garde propositions of theoretical physics (such as 'string theory') will be regarded as 'interesting', if the position of the proponent within the scientific hierarchy be sufficiently high (or should he have friends in high places), and his behaviour be appropriate to requirements. Otherwise, his work is poor, preposterous or even fraudulent. Should he not be a member of that organisation, he is a heretic, and unworthy of any attention; in which case, he is just plainly ignored. Not even the word 'charlatan' will be applied.

This brief review of the judgmental aspect of science is not inappropriate. Callinan[7], who has reviewed many physical studies of homoeopathic preparations, comments that 'In spite of the impressive array of equipment, the experimental designs and analysis are generally poor, with no presentation of statistical data, and limited provision for reproducibility.' Now, believe it or not, Callinan is actually a proponent of homoeopathy and not an opponent; he is just being plain honest. And whilst some of us may regard such experiments, therefore, as being totally invalid, others may feel that they are at least an indication of the physical foundation we seek. Again it is a matter of viewpoint and prejudice. Endler[11], rather kindly, states that '… (the) diagnostic tools … need to be further refined'; and even Callinan concludes that 'The results are generally supportive.' They certainly are to be regarded as 'interesting'.

The investigations that have been carried out include measurements of electrical conductivity, relative permittivity (dielectric constant) and surface tension. Additionally, and perhaps more importantly, there have been used NMR (nuclear magnetic resonance) spectroscopes, Raman laser spectroscopes, UV (ultraviolet) spectroscopes and light polarizers. Some of the more important studies will be considered, beginning with some relatively simple electrical experiments.

Two of these involve measurement of the *relative permittivity* (formerly termed the *dielectric constant*)[7]. Gay and Boiron (1951–1953), studying distilled water to which had been added a small quantity of Sodium chloride 27c, found that they could select the single bottle containing this potency from 99 control bottles containing distilled water alone. Stephenson and Brucato (1966) studied Mercuric chloride 1x to 33x, prepared in distilled water. For the controls (distilled water alone), the relative permittivity varied from 5.60 to 6.05, whereas, for the homoeopathic preparations, it varied from 2.80 to 4.40.

Resch, Gutmann and Schauer[21](1982) found that dilute sodium chloride solutions revealed an increase in *electrical conductivity* by rocking them prior to measurement.

Wurmser and Loch[7] (1948), studying the intensity and wavelength of light by *photoelectric cell,* found measurable differences between several substances from 24x to 30x.

Smith and Boericke[29] (1974) investigated diluent structure by means of *NMR spectroscopy* with regard to various dilutions of Sulphur up to 30x in ethanol-water. Unsuccussed dilutions were compared with those that had been succussed, those that had been subjected to ultrasonic vibration, and ethanol-water controls. The identified structural changes selectively involved OH (hydroxyl) groups. They found differences in the OH group of the spectrum of the unsuccussed, succussed and ultrasonic Sulphur dilutions when compared with the controls, with little if any change in the CH_3 and CH_2 alcohol groups. Considered in more detail:

(1) Diluent structure was changed in unsuccussed serial dilutions when compared with undiluted diluent.

(2) Diluent structure was further changed by succussion of serial dilutions when compared to unsuccussed dilutions and undiluted diluent.

(3) These changes became more extreme as the dilutions approached and exceeded the point of absence of all molecules of the intended solute.

(4) Ultrasonic potencies were associated with structural changes more like those of succussed rather than those of unsuccussed serial dilutions.

Lastly, Boiron and Vinh[6] (1976), using *Raman laser spectroscopy,* have shown that, for the 1c potency of Kalium bichromicum (potassium bichromate, $K_2Cr_2O_7$), the spectrum of alcohol disappears almost totally when that of potassium bichromate appears. In Kalium bichromicum 1c, the ratio of the number of bichromate molecules to that of alcohol molecules is 1 to 500. In this case, therefore, the light meets 500 more alcohol molecules than those of bichromate, and yet the alcohol spectrum does not appear. This suggests the possibility that the alcohol molecules have been so changed as to produce a Raman laser spectrum typical of potassium bichromate.

Since investigations such as these command no apparent financial rewards for either the individual or the pharmaceutical companies, and since their results are predictively spurious in terms of current orthodox theory, they have only, and regrettably, been pursued in a limited and under-funded manner. They also have been either treated with an undeserved contempt, or subjected to a supercilious denial by astigmatic and myopic parrots, who rest on higher and gilded perches, and who shed their ill-conceived droppings on the heads of their own sycophants. You might ask yourselves, therefore, whether such birds are not a greater hazard to health than Galileo's pizzas?

Element XII

'Dig for Victory!'

In view of the failure of the dynamic field theories of potentisation to offer a complete explanation of that process, we must now excavate to a lower stratum of matter and turn to the *submolecular theories*.

Whereas the experimental observations quoted previously are subject to a number of possible interpretations, we shall see that those that derive from *spectroscopy* do offer some plausible clues to the way in which the inductive chemical imprint of the solute might be carried in the diluent.

The key to such specific representation must lie somewhere in the diluent molecule; either in the atoms of which it is composed or the bonds between them. In fact, we have to consider three major diluents in homoeopathy, viz. water, ethanol and lactose. In this respect, you might recall (from Element III) that it was mentioned that, in actual practice, it is quite difficult to provide either ethanol or lactose that is totally free of water. Nevertheless, it seems extremely unlikely that the small amount of water 'contaminating' these substances can be held totally responsible for the inductive chemical imprint. It would appear, therefore, that we should search for some factor common to all three diluents.

With regard to this, the experiment of Smith and Boericke[29] (1974) quoted in Element XI, involving NMR spectroscopy, gives us a hint. They suggested that changes in OH groups of ethanol-water were of some significance in the process of potentisation, and, as luck would have it, all three diluents possess *OH groups* (the water molecule itself is essentially a bifurcate OH group). In order to make some sense out of the matter, we are obliged to examine not only the O–H bond itself, but also the non-bonding electronic configuration of oxygen and the nuclear structure of both constituent atoms. It will become apparent that our analysis will be usefully combined with certain elements of dynamic field theory, in order to produce a cohesive and realistic 'conclusive' theory of potentisation. This, of course, cannot be formulated in isolation from an appraisal of the biological effects of both homoeopathic remedies and drugs, and the conceptualisation of how they might induce these changes.

Element XIII

Back to basics

In order to understand which properties of the solute might be specifically and usefully imprinted upon the diluent, and how this might be achieved, we are obliged to examine the finer properties of matter.

Surprising as it may seem, the nucleus of an atom, which accounts for most of its mass, has a diameter of only 1/100,000th of the overall atomic diameter as defined by the path of the outermost electron. Putting this into perspective, if the Earth were imagined to be an atom, then its central nucleus would be a globe only 120 metres in diameter having a mass of about 6×10^{24}kg! The nucleus itself spins, and consists of varying numbers of protons and neutrons, according to the element and its isotopic configuration. In the case of basic *hydrogen*, the nucleus is composed of a single proton. The protons each carry a single standard unit of positive electric charge.

Outside the nucleus are the electrons, each carrying a single unit of negative charge, and the electromagnetic field that exists between them and the nucleus. In the *Bohr model* of the atom, the electrons move in definite *orbits* around the nucleus, rather like moons around a planet, and only certain orbits are 'allowable' of particular radii from the centre of the atom. The larger the radius (that is to say, the higher the orbit), the greater is the energy of the orbiting electron.

This somewhat simplistic model of the 'celestial' electron has, however, been replaced by the historically more recent tenets of *Schrödinger's wave mechanics*[3]. Here, the electron is said to move within an *orbital*, rather than an orbit, which is essentially a three-dimensional space in which there is a greater-than-zero probability of finding it somewhere. This is often illustrated by means of a boundary diagram showing the shape and position (relative to the nuclear centre) of the space corresponding to 90–95% probability of finding the electron. Orbitals come in a variety of shapes, sizes and positions. Some are spherical, some are like two pears coupled together at their stalks, and other varieties exist. The situation is rather like that of an unbroken egg, where we cannot be certain of the exact position of the yolk, but can be assured that it is somewhere to be found within the space defined by the egg-shell. Different orbitals may also overlap each other. Despite these embellishments, the basic principles of the Bohr model with respect to energy of the electron remain, merely substituting the word *orbital* for *orbit*. Each orbital is associated with a particular electron energy, and only certain orbitals are 'allowable'. When an electron is 'promoted' by the application of appropriate energy, this *excitation* causes it to jump from the lower orbital to the next higher, without any intermediate positions being manifest. Its energetic state is thus discontinuous or *quantised*. When it returns to the lower orbital, again by a 'quantum jump', a quantum of electromagnetic radiation is released, termed a *photon*, which, viewed in the form of a wave, bears a frequency characteristic of the orbital translocation that has occurred (remember that the principle of *wave-particle duality* 'allows' us to say that electromagnetic radiation has the properties of both particles [photons] and waves).

The energetic arrangement of the electrons within a given atom is dependent on such factors as proton-electron attraction, electron-electron repulsion, electron shielding (where the inner electrons shield the outer from the protonic attraction), and the fact that no more than two electrons can occupy any particular orbital (in accordance with the *Pauli exclusion principle*). Although orbitals of similar geometry and position are given the same labels with respect to different atoms (e.g. $1s$, $2p$), the important point is that their energetic status differs according to the element. This is best explained in terms of the *periodic table (of elements)*, which is arranged in vertical *groups* and horizontal *periods*. As we move down a group, so the atoms become larger. This is not only because more orbital shells are added, but also because the outer electrons are increasingly shielded from attraction of the nucleus by the inner electrons. As we move from left to right across a period, the number of orbital shells stays the same, but the number of protons in the nucleus increases. This results in the nucleus exerting a stronger attraction on the electrons, thus causing their orbitals to contract towards the nucleus. Consequently, the atoms get progressively smaller as we pass along the period. Indeed, the fundamental energetic configuration of the orbitals is unique to each atom. Additionally, upon the loss or gain of one or more electrons to form an ion, yet another unique set of orbital electronic energies is created.

When atoms bond together to form molecules, further energetic changes occur, including the formation of bonding (and 'antibonding') orbitals of different shapes. According to the *molecular orbital theory*, the electrons of the entire molecule come under the influence of each other and the constituent nuclei. In this manner, the electrons of the various atoms that comprise the molecule tend to lose their energetic identity, with the formation of a new set of orbitals of energetic individuality. Speaking generally, we may divide the electronic configuration of any atom into two groups: a central group of *noble gas* configuration (e.g. helium, neon, argon), and an outer group of *valency* electrons (hydrogen is an exception in that it only possesses one electron). From the purely chemical viewpoint, the reactivity of an atom is greatly determined by the number and energies of the valency group (although we must not forget that the charge of the atom is also of some significance when it becomes an ion). Similarly, the number and energies of the electrons of the higher orbitals is relevant when considering the reactivity of a diatomic or polyatomic molecule. Of course, not all of the available valency electrons become involved in interatomic bonding, and oxygen, for example, in the water molecule has two *lone pairs* of non-bonding electrons.

The main point of importance to be gleaned from this discussion, is that the higher orbitals of a particular atom or molecule not only influence its chemical reactivity, but also possess a unique energetic status peculiar to that entity of matter.

Legal counterfeiting

Based upon the chemical reactivity and individuality of the higher atomic, ionic or molecular orbitals, Sharma[24,25,26] has proposed a submolecular theory of some considerable appeal. However, as we shall see, it has a number of flaws which must be overcome, and in so doing we shall come to some surprising conclusions with regard to energy storage at the atomic level.

Let us endeavour to put Sharma's cogent proposals in the simplest terms, avoiding a discussion of such concepts as electron 'spin' (which has nothing to do with spinning motion at all), and orbital 'hybridization' and 'dehybridization' (which Sharma discusses, but tend to be confusing for most readers), all of which are unnecessary for a basic comprehension of his concepts.

During succussion or trituration, the highest electronic (valency) orbitals of the solute molecule comes in close proximity to the diluent molecule (water, ethanol or lactose). The supplied mechanical energy then causes a number (from one to four) of the *lone pair* electrons of the *oxygen* atom of the *OH group* to be *resonantly promoted* to a new orbital status possessing the energies characteristic of those of the highest orbitals of the solute. In this way, the oxygen lone pair electrons now adopt chemical reactive properties typical of the solute which has influenced them. Or do they? We shall see.

In support of this theory of potentisation, which we may term the *orbital energy theory*, are quoted two of the spectroscopic experiments outlined in Element XI, to which you might wish to refer. Firstly, that of Smith and Boericke[29] (1974), which indicated definite changes in the OH spectrum with potentisation; and secondly, that of Boiron and Vinh[6] (1976), concerning the spectral properties of Kalium bichromicum lc. Sharma also refers to Sankaran, who cites that the French physicist Gustave de Bon demonstrated that Sodium chloride 1M (1000c) produced the spectrum of sodium when sprayed into a vacuum. This anecdote, however, is seriously flawed by the fact that most potencies are prepared in soda glass, and leaching of sodium ions into the preparation occurs, especially during succussion. We are not informed whether this particular remedy was prepared in neutral glass or soda glass. This observation, as far as it goes, may, therefore, be taken with a pinch of salt.

One of the main objections to the orbital energy theory concerns basic chemistry. If the diluent molecule d_m, through lone pair promotion, can simulate the chemical reactivities of a solute molecule, atom or ion m, then it should be possible to demonstrate *in vitro* and by means of non-biological experimentation that d_m has acquired some chemical properties characteristic of m and uncharacteristic of an ordinary diluent molecule d. Infinitesimal potencies of, for example, either blood or manganese oxide (MnO_2) should be able to catalyse the release of oxygen from hydrogen peroxide (H_2O_2). Apparently, however, this is not the case. So, if the orbital energy theory is correct, what is the explanation?

The chemical reactivity of m is not only determined by its valency electrons and their orbital energies, but also by the electric *charge* that it bears. As will be discussed later, in potentising sodium chloride (Na^+Cl^-), of potentised molecules d_m we would expect 50% to acquire the higher orbital characteristics of $Na+$ and 50% to acquire those of Cl^-. The ion Na^+ bears one full unit of positive charge, but the corresponding diluent molecule d_{Na^+} does not. Where d_{Na^+} is water, it bears a small negative charge $\delta-$ (<1) at its oxygen pole, and small positive charges $\delta+$ (<1) at its hydrogen poles. Similar observations naturally apply with regard to Cl^- and d_{Cl^-}.

The charge, its intensity or its distribution in d_m is always different from that of m. Even if m is non-ionic, non-polar or electrically polarised, this must be so. In the case of a non-ionic, non-polar molecule, such as S_8 (sulphur), it will be represented by a polar molecule of diluent, and thus will now bear the imprint of electrical charge. This electrical difference between d_m and m is of paramount importance in determining the different chemicoreactive properties of the two. It serves to explain why infinitesimal doses of the remedy *Natrum muriaticum* (which, although prepared from rock-salt, is largely a derivative of sodium chloride) can exert a *pharmacological* effect. Whereas, for most purposes, small amounts of Na^+Cl^- must be regarded as therapeutically inert, with Na^+ being largely excluded from the cell by the sodium-potassium *ionic* pump, on the other hand, d_{Na^+}, which is *non-ionic* (and, therefore, not recognised by the pump) is not so excluded and can produce profound physiological changes. This statement should naturally lead us to examine the ways in which remedies act in the biological situation, but, for convenience, we shall leave this matter in abeyance for the moment, and return to the orbital energy theory proper.

A second reason for differing reactivity between d_m and m, more relevant to the biochemical situation, is that the shapes and sizes of the molecules are unlikely to correspond. Certainly with regard to many drugs, the ability of them to key geometrically into the receptor site determines at least part of their biochemical potential.

The plot thickens

Another point of chemicoreactive dissimilarity between the potentised diluent molecule d_m and its inductive solute molecule m concerns their ability to form covalent or ionic bonds, and thus new compounds .

If m *is* composed of two covalently bonded atoms, such as CuO (black copper oxide), that bond must be broken in reactions such as:

$$CuO + H_2SO_4 \rightarrow CuSO_4 + H_2O$$

However, the equivalent potentised diluent molecule d_{CuO}, in that its *core structure* maintains its integrity, has no such potential for splitting into two molecules, d_{Cu} and d_O.

The other important point concerns the energetic stability of the promoted lone pair electrons. In the formation of a bond between two atoms, the contributing electrons adopt new and characteristic energy levels (bonding and 'antibonding' orbitals). According to the *collision theory* of chemical reactions, sufficient collisional energy must be supplied to initiate the process. The application of such energy will cause the promoted lone pair electrons of d_m to 'depromote'. They will, however, not depromote to the bonding level of energy characteristic of a particular m reaction, but will return to their normal unpotentised *ground state* within the diluent molecule (d_m thus becomes an ordinary molecule d again). This energetic instability is highly prohibitive of the formation of aberrant compounds between d_m and substances which are readily chemically reactive with m.

Indeed, the relative instability of molecules d_m *is* demonstrated in two ways. Firstly, their inactivation by *ultraviolet radiation* (UVR), and secondly their inactivation by strong *magnetic fields*. Remedies exposed to such influences readily become therapeutically inert.

The inactivation by UVR (which explains why potentised remedies should be kept away from sunlight) is, in itself, strongly confirmatory of the orbital energy theory of potentisation. After all, UV spectroscopy is used to investigate valency-shell electrons, since these are energised by UV frequencies. As I have remarked, appropriate energisation of promoted lone pair electrons will tend to depromote them to their natural ground state. What could, therefore, be more appropriate than UVR to do the job?

Neither is it surprising to learn of the deleterious effect of magnetism, which, in sufficient strength, could readily depose an electron in an exalted and precarious position and strip it of its privileges.

In fact, if the orbital energy theory were correct, by what mechanism could the promoted electrons exhibit the property of *metastability* rather than that of gross instability? Certainly remedies prepared with reasonable amounts of ethanol, and lactose triturates will maintain their potency for years when kept unexposed to UVR and strong magnetic fields.

In order to answer this question, we must also consider another matter, which itself is an objection to the orbital energy theory, and one which must be overcome. As Callinan[8] has implied, it is unlikely that energy supplied by succussion is delivered at a rate sufficient to influence the electronic status of the diluent molecule. This is perhaps why many have chosen to ignore this laudable theory. However, as we shall discover, things, like politicians, are not always what they might seem.

Quarks don't have quirks

Whilst it is possible to conceive that each stroke of vigorous trituration might supply enough energy to lactose to promote the lone pair electrons of its hydroxyl groups, it is more difficult to see how each shake or blow of succussion (an altogether less energetic process) might achieve the same for water or ethanol. Here, in any event, much of the applied energy is dissipated in inducing unproductive translatory motion of the molecules of the liquid potency and the rupture of hydrogen bonds. Such does not apply to any significant degree with regard to trituration.

Electronic excitation and promotion could only occur if there were some way of storing the energy of each shake or blow of succussion. There is nothing, unfortunately, in modern conventional physics to assist us in this matter. Yet we shall not be deterred, and reflect that neither does it admit to the existence of an infinitesimal remedy, which must exist because it has been shown to act in the clinical or biological situation.

There is, fortuitously, a great deal of evidence that water can store large amounts of energy in a way that is indeterminable in terms of current physics. I am referring, in fact, to the matter of *cold (nuclear) fusion*. It appears that certain methods of electrolysis can produce surplus energy from either deuterium oxide, as Fleischmann and Pons[18] have demonstrated, or common water, as determined by others. This, as with all heretical discoveries[23], has been met with the customary dissent of orthodox and unimaginative physicists, and, rather like homoeopathy, has been condemned for its originality. Nevertheless, despite the inability of its protagonists to satisfy the rigours of peer analysis, which is as ridiculous as that in medicine (where, in the main, the blind assess the partially-sighted as to their vision), large companies have seen it fit to invest great amounts of money in its development, being more impressed with what they have seen than what they think should be seen in terms of rigid scientific thought.

After all, what peer is it who knows less than his so-called equal? The main feature, apart from the release of 'occult' energy from water or its isotopic form, is that there is little or no radioactivity released in the process, and whereas its proponents have labelled it as *cold fusion,* they, who are to be credited with its discovery and development, have only done so in ignorance of its true nature and in order to make it appear within the bounds of normal science. Actually, it is extremely unlikely to be a fusion process at all, just as the opponents of the phenomenon have proclaimed, and, if indeed it exists, as it undoubtedly does, then it is the product of something unthought of hitherto.

It would appear, on the face of it, extremely unlikely that the energy storage we seek could be the responsibility of the electrons themselves, for they would seem to either accept energy and jump to a higher orbital, or totally reject it, when it is inappropriate or insufficient, and stay put in their ground state. Perhaps a lone pair electron could slowly, albeit discontinuously, rise to the *target orbital* as determined by an outer electron of the solute molecule *m*. However, whilst for every quantum of energy stored there would be a small displacement of the electron centrifugally, should it be insufficiently energised to reach its target orbital, it would then persist (though metastably) in an orbital totally uncharacteristic of *m*, and, therefore, would be entirely without energetic correspondence. Indeed, it would represent some totally different substance; a fact which would not go unrecognised therapeutically.

We might, therefore, turn our attention to the atomic nucleus, and see what might be fathomed. This is composed of protons and neutrons; although the hydrogen nucleus is essentially a plain and simple, single proton. Both the proton and the neutron are believed to be composed of three *quarks.* The relevant quarks are termed *up* (bearing a charge of $+\frac{2}{3}$) and *down* (bearing a charge of $-\frac{1}{3}$). The proton consists of two *up* quarks and one *down* (charge: $\frac{2}{3} + \frac{2}{3} - \frac{1}{3} = +1$), whereas the neutron consists of one *up* and two *down* (charge: $\frac{2}{3} - \frac{1}{3} - \frac{1}{3} = 0$). Is it not possible that somewhere in the quarks of which the nuclei of the hydroxyl groups are composed are sub-particles that could store energy? Unfortunately, all my attempts to construct a satisfactory model upon this basis have been thwarted by immense theoretical difficulties, and which, in order to be overcome, have led to an hypothesis so complex as to be untenable. Once again, therefore, but not reluctantly, we must turn our attention to the electron.

During mechanical energisation, a solute molecule (or ion) *m* is forced into close proximity with an ordinary diluent molecule *d*. It is proposed that some of the energy of this collision is utilised to produce certain *virtual particles*, which, by definition, are only observable or measurable in terms of their effect, and not directly (quantum theorists should have little objection to such a concept, since it is popularly used by them). These virtual particles communicate energetic information from the electrons of the higher orbitals of m to the lone pair electrons of the hydroxyl group or groups of d. As with other particles, such as light photons or electrons, these virtual particles, which we may term *orbitons*, have the properties of both particles and waves (in accordance with the principle of *wave-particle duality*). Accordingly, they can readily be conceptualised as being both little packets or quanta of energy and waves, each with a frequency that conveys the energetic status of an outer electron of m to the lone pair electrons of d. Since they are virtual particles, by definition we have no way of directly measuring what that frequency might be. However, we might infer that those frequencies would be in the ultraviolet range, since such frequencies are associated with energetic changes in outer electrons. In this way, we might conceptualise the orbiton as a type of *virtual ultraviolet photon*. Whereas a *real* or measurable ultraviolet photon is only released by an outer electron of the molecule (or ion) m when it spontaneously returns to a lower level after energetic excitation to a higher orbital, there is no such requirement for the production of a virtual ultraviolet photon or orbiton. In this manner, the orbiton must be conceived as a particle of lower energetic status than its real or measurable counterpart.

These orbitons become attached to the lone pair electrons, and when a sufficient number of identical frequency (when viewed as waves) have been accumulated on a particular electron, then the electron will jump to the appropriate target orbital (corresponding to the energy of the appropriate higher orbital of m), thus contributing to the change of the diluent molecule from d to d_m.

According to this theory, therefore, an electron may exist in an *intermediate* state of energisation, where despite the accumulation of what amounts to *potential energy*, it still remains in its conventional lower orbital. In that case, there should be some evidence for such a change in terms of the behaviour of the electron. If you would reexamine the NMR experiment of Smith and Boericke[29] (1974), quoted in Element Xl, you will find that diluent structure, with regard to OH groups, was changed in *unsuccussed* serial dilutions as compared with ordinary diluent. This rather strange phenomenon can be explained on the basis of *intermediate electronic excitation*, in that the very act of producing a solution or its minor agitation imparts sufficient energy for this to occur; a level of energy far too small to induce direct electronic orbital promotion.

The atomic implications of electronic energy adsorption are more fully discusssed in Element XXII.

Shake, rattle or roll?

It has been described how a lone pair electron of the oxygen atom of the diluent hydroxyl group might adsorb energy. This adsorption is not, however, limited to its occupation of the lower orbital, but may also occur after it has been promoted to its higher *target orbital*. Although this promoted position is *metastable* in nature, a liquid potency may be stabilised almost indefinitely by occasional agitation. As professional homoeopathic pharmacists are aware, the delivery of the odd shake, or blow of succussion, even at relatively infrequent intervals (say, once monthly), will preserve the therapeutic efficacy of the remedy for many, many years. One possible reason for this is the adsorption of energy by the promoted lone pair electrons.

The production of an *inductive chemical imprint* has thus far been considered in relation to the collision of a solute molecule m and a diluent molecule d. The same principles, by extension, apply to the collision of an imprinted or 'promoted' diluent molecule d_m and a virgin, unimprinted or 'unpromoted' diluent molecule d. Hence, even as molecules m are progressively removed by serial dilution, and even beyond the point at which they are no longer present, their higher orbital energies continue to be mechanically impressed on d via the molecules d_m.

The number of molecules d converted to d_m will depend on the total quantity of kinetic (mechanical) energy delivered during each successive episode after each phase of serial dilution. The more aggressive or more prolonged the method of succussion, the greater will be the number of imprinted diluent molecules produced. However, not all the applied kinetic energy induces the collision of m or d_m with d. Some is wasted in ineffectual collisions of m with m or d_m (in the lower dilutions), d_m with d_m, and d with d. Other fractions of the applied kinetic energy are concerned with the breaking of surface tension and the rupture of the hydrogen bonds linking the molecules of diluent. These effects, however, are contributory to the 'promotion' of the diluent, in that they encourage the freer collision of the molecules.

A matter which sometimes puzzles students of homoeopathy is why the molecules of the glass vial (silica, etc.) do not impose their imprint to any significant degree upon the diluent. Fortunately, this is not too difficult to explain. In the first place, the inner surface of any glass vessel is not microscopically smooth. Molecules of both diluent and solute are trapped by small crevices and irregularities, and thus form an *interfacial molecular layer* which denies the direct collision of translating molecules with those of the glass. This is so for both *soda glass*, and the less common and more expensive *neutral glass*. In fact, soda glass produces a better interfacial molecular layer than its neutral counterpart. Soda glass bears a negative electric charge at its surface, which electrostatically attracts polar molecules and cations (positive ions). Both water and ethanol are, as we have said, polar solvents, and many substances used to produce remedies are comprised of polar molecules or ions. Water molecules, for example, will become fixed to the soda glass by means of their positively-charged hydrogen poles. Soda glass thus produces a more impermeable collisional barrier than neutral glass. However, the disadvantage, if it can be deemed so, of soda glass is that sodium ions are leached from it, which, therefore, contaminate the liquid potency. Since soda glass is preferentially used in homoeopathic pharmacy (because it is both traditional and cheaper), it follows that virtually all liquid potencies are contaminated with sodium ions and any 'promoted' molecules of diluent that stem therefrom. However, so small is their contribution to the overall remedy, in clinical practice, that their effect is negligible or unapparent.

With regard to trituration by mortar and pestle (or any equivalent mechanical device), the adherence of a layer of lactose molecules to the surfaces of the apparatus similarly protects the bulk of the preparation from undue direct collision with ceramic or metallic molecules. Again, however, a small, but insignificant, level of contamination will occur by some loss of the latter molecules from the grinding surfaces, which, to a minor degree, become involved in the process of lactose energisation.

Gift tokens in medical practice

By invoking the concept of energy storage on lone pair electrons, we are able to make certain important inferences with regard to potentisation.

The first of these concerns the degree to which the major components of the original substance impress themselves on the diluent.

The second concerns the role of minor molecular or ionic constituents, including contaminants, of the original substance undergoing potentisation, and that of contaminants in the diluent; some of which, as we have noted, may arise from the potentising vessel, and others from the atmosphere. Those from the atmosphere include the ever-present dissolved gases, various particles of dust, and even bacteria and fungal spores. The use of higher concentrations of ethanol must destroy or inhibit the latter, but our main concern here is whether they make any significant contribution to the ultimate remedy.

Perhaps the simplest notion is that any molecule or ion will imprint the diluent in direct proportion to its initial relative molar concentration: that is to say, at the stage of the first serial dilution (1x or 1c). The relative molar concentration (RMC) is calculated by dividing the molar concentration (moles/litre) of the molecule or ion under consideration by the total molar concentration of all molecules and ions in solution, and multiplying by 100, in order to express it as a percentage. Let us consider a solution in which the solute is composed of two molecular species, *ma* and *mb*. For a molecule *ma*, with an initial RMC of 80%, we might expect that 80% of 'promoted' diluent molecules would be d_{ma}; and for a molecule *mb*, with an initial RMC of 20%, the expected figure for d_{mb} would be 20% (a ratio of 4:1). Let us now see why this is *incorrect*.

In producing these numerical conclusions, we have actually made two assumptions. The first of these, which is probably correct, is that a molecule d_m can only represent a *single* species of molecule or ion. In potentising, say,

Na+Cl− (sodium chloride), only d_{Na^+} and d_{Cl^-} are 'allowable', and $d_{Na^+Cl^-}$ is 'disallowed'. This is because the lone pair electrons cannot engineer compromise promoted orbitals between two or more molecular or ionic species, and are obliged to select only one set. The second assumption we have made in our computation is that each collision is so effective as to promote the lone pair electrons directly to their target orbitals. If that were the case, the figures with regard to d_m would hold true. However, as we have discussed, succussion is unlikely to induce this direct promotion, in that it is insufficiently energetic. Energy must be stored in stages upon the electron before promotion can occur. As we shall see in the discussion that follows, the laws of *probability*, when applied to such *progressive quantised energisation*, significantly alter the figures. The alternative second assumption that we might have made concerns the possibility of *repotentisation*, but this again depends upon direct electronic promotion. The idea is that a molecule d_{ma} when involved in a collision with *mb is* converted to d_{mb}. In this way, all solute molecules and ions have a chance of proportional representation. However, in terms of the present theory, the promoted electron cannot switch from one target orbital directly to another. In order to achieve this, it must first be 'depromoted' to its ground state. In other words, direct repotentisation is 'disallowed'.

In order to simplify matters, yet not distort the truth excessively, we shall assume that our succussive energy is such that only one orbiton is released from the highest orbital of either *ma* or *mb* during collision with *d*, and that only pure collisions of either *ma* or *mb* with *d* occur (and not combined collisions of all three). We shall also assume that only one lone pair electron of *d* must be ultimately promoted to its target orbital as determined by either of these two solute species. For the sake of brevity, this electron is denoted as 'E*'.

Let us initially examine the rules that govern the activity of E*. In order to be promoted to a particular target orbital, E* must collect a definite number of energetic quanta of an identical type; that is to say, orbitons of the same frequency and energy (for the purposes of the illustration given after, I have arbitrarily put this number of quanta at three). Rather like collecting gift tokens from garages, it cannot mix those from Esso with those from Shell and expect to receive something in the post. Unlike the average motorist, E* also suffers from limited storage capacity. It can only hold a certain amount of energy, and must reject any surplus. In terms of the theory under discussion, this energy level should be slightly above the highest level required for electronic promotion. Because different orbitons have different frequencies, their energy also differs; so we cannot define the storage capacity of E* in terms of an exact number of quanta for all circumstances. However, for the sake of argument, we shall assume that the energies of the two species of orbiton from *ma* and *mb* are fairly close, and arbitrarily say that the maximum allowable number of stored quanta on E* is four.

You will recall that the ratio of solute molecules *ma* to *mb* is 4:1 (80%:20%). In inducing our first set of collisions, of those energised molecules d_m, we should expect 4 out of 5 to have adsorbed a single orbiton (denoted as 'pA') from *ma* and 1 out of 5 to have adsorbed a single orbiton (denoted 'pB') from *mb*. This is a result of simple probability analysis.

What happens next is rather like assessing the probability of throwing two consecutive 'sixes' with a die. The probability of throwing the first one is, of course, ⅙ (0.167). The probability of throwing a six followed by another six is ⅙ × ⅙, in other words ¹⁄₃₆ (0.028).

To return to our main problem, we must calculate the effect of probability on our next set of induced collisions. The probability of a diluent molecule that has already adsorbed one orbiton pA adsorbing another of the same (terming this state 'pA/pA') is ⅘ × ⅘, or ¹⁶⁄₂₅ (0.640). In contrast, the probability of a diluent molecule that has already adsorbed one orbiton pB adsorbing the same ('pB/pB') is ⅕ × ⅕ or ¹⁄₂₅ (0.040). Considering the probabilities now of a third collision producing either pA/pA/pA or pB/pB/pB, the respective figures are (⅘)³ and (⅕)³. In other words, these are ⁶⁴⁄₁₂₅ (0.512) and ¹⁄₁₂₅ (0.008). Since we have arbitrarily set the number of identical quanta required for electronic promotion at three, we can now assess the ratio of d_{ma} to d_{mb}, where only three sets of collision are allowed. The ratio is 64:1, which is drastically different from the 4:1 predicted on the basis of electron promotion in one step. This clearly suggests that the random accumulation of energetic quanta selects the dominant molecular or ionic species for major representation in the diluent, and that it acts unfavourably for those present in lesser amounts (including contaminants). Nevertheless, as we shall see, with the progression of potentisation, this effect is attenuated, but by no means disappears.

In practice, we are allowed more sets of collision than three. So far we have only considered the case of those molecules of diluent which can actually be 'promoted' in three stages. What of the other energised diluent molecules which have the mixed conformations 2pA/pB (probability ⁴⁸⁄₁₂₅ = 0.384) or pA/2pB (probability ¹²⁄₁₂₅ = 0.096)? At the fourth collision, we will add either pA or pB to either, leading to 3pA/pB (probability ¹⁹²⁄₆₂₅ = 0.307) in the first case, pA/3pB (probability ¹²⁄₆₂₅ = 0.019) in the second, or 2pA/2pB (probability ⁹⁶⁄₆₂₅ = 0.154) in either (in calculating these probabilities, I have allowed for the ineffectual collisions of either *ma* or *mb* with the previously 'promoted' molecules, and, for simplicity, not permitted the latter to collide with other diluent molecules). The conformation $3\mathrm{p}A/\mathrm{p}B$ will lead to 'promotion' to d_{ma} and $\mathrm{p}A/3\mathrm{p}B$ will lead to 'promotion' to d_{mb}. The ratio of total d_{ma} to d_{mb} is now approximately 30:1. The surplus energetic quanta, $\mathrm{p}B$ and $\mathrm{p}A$ respectively, will be discarded (to yield kinetic energy, heat, etc.). The remaining conformation $2\mathrm{p}A/2\mathrm{p}B$ cannot be promoted until an appropriate orbitonic quantum is received; yet E^* is saturated, since it cannot store more than four such quanta. Upon receipt of either $\mathrm{p}A$ or $\mathrm{p}B$ from a fifth collision, it will immediately be promoted to the appropriate target orbital, discarding a quantum of either $\mathrm{p}A$ or $\mathrm{p}B$ accordingly. The ratio of total d_{ma} to d_{mb} is now in the order of 17:1. This is obviously quite different from the ratio of 4:1 which we might have intuitively deduced from that of the solute molecules or ions. These figures, of course, should not be taken too literally, and merely serve to exemplify the basis of a theory which proposes that the random accumulation of energetic quanta (orbitons) leads to preferential non-proportional representation of the dominant constituents of the solute.

Where molecules or ions are present in equimolar concentrations, their representation within the diluent should also be equal (in fact, as we shall see in Element XXIII, this is not always the case). Hence, Na^+Cl^- should be represented by d_{Na^+} and d_{Cl^-} in equal quantities.

Of course, as serial dilution proceeds, the original solute molecules or ions are progressively removed, and ultimately disappear. Does this mean that diluent or atmospheric contaminants of the liquid potency can then impose their nature more effectively upon the diluent? On the contrary; for whereas the initially dominant solute molecules themselves are removed, they are replaced by d_{m} molecules, which are equally competitive.

So far we have considered the case of a single orbiton being released during collision. How will things change if we induce the release of $2\mathrm{p}A$ or $2\mathrm{p}B$ instead as a result of stronger successive energy being applied? E^* now only requires one further quantum to complete a set of three. The chances of this occurring for $E^*[2\mathrm{p}A]$ are $\frac{4}{5} \times \frac{4}{5}$ or $\frac{16}{25}$ (0.640). For $E^*[2\mathrm{p}B]$ they are $\frac{1}{5} \times \frac{1}{5}$ or $\frac{1}{25}$ (0.040). This demonstrates that the probability of a molecule or ion being represented improves with the force of succussion. Therefore, the way in which we succuss varies the ultimate properties of the remedy; a surprising but logical, consequence of our analysis.

The implications of this conclusion are not only most interesting, but also have a profound bearing on homoeopathic pharmaceutical technique. If we succuss by solely agitating the contents of the vial, then we are less likely to produce an effective concentration of molecules d_{m} which carry the inductive chemical imprint of lesser constituents of our original substance. At the same time, all contaminants will be effectively excluded from representation. On the other hand, if we succuss with the usual method of agitation followed by a successive *blow* against the hand or a leather-bound book, then we will produce a remedy that has a reasonable expression of the lesser constituents of the original substance, but with a greater likelihood of contaminant influence. However, provided we are meticulous in the preparation of our original substance, and in preserving the purity of our diluent and working atmosphere, the more aggressive method of potentisation is generally more advantageous, in that we obtain a better overall chemical imprint of the various facets of our original material. Nevertheless, where it is our intention to sort the wheat from the chaff, and produce a remedy which conveys only the nature of the dominant molecules, the method of simple agitation is better. This might occur, for example, where some rare plant has been gathered, but has been heavily contaminated with mud or dust, and cannot be completely cleaned with water. Succussion by means of agitation alone will render it less likely that any residual mud or dust exerts any significant effect on the properties of the preparation.

In Element XI, we noted that the experiment of Smith and Boericke[29] suggested that ultrasonic agitation appeared to produce effects similar to that of conventional succussion. Certainly this phenomenon is worthy of further investigation, in that we might more carefully regulate the intensity of delivery of energy to the vial and its contents.

Forbidden fruit

A particular point of elegance of the *orbital energy theory* and its various riders is their ability to explain how 'unwanted' substances are denied representation, either fully or partially.

We have already explored one such mechanism in Element XVIII, concerning the preferential representation of dominant molecules or ions.

However, there is another proposed mechanism equally worthy of attention. In this respect, I must draw your attention to the fact that ethanol does not impress its character on water, and vice versa. Let us suppose that we have produced a number of serial dilutions of a particular substance using 14% ethanol-water. Having reached the potency of 29c, we wish to stabilise the remedy, for the purposes of sterility and longevity, by the addition of 95% alcohol. The 30th centesimal potency is now, therefore, composed almost entirely of ethanol molecules, whereas the previous potencies were dominantly water. Even if we had produced the 30th centesimal with 14% ethanol, a freshly prepared potency would have no discernible differences in clinical effect from that prepared with the stronger alcohol. This can only be so if the ethanol does not imprint itself upon the water. You might ask yourselves, what might be the basis of this enigma?

The simplest explanation, and perhaps the closest one to the truth, is that certain target orbitals for lone pair electrons are 'forbidden'; that is to say, they are unattainable. Even in conventional physics, the notion of the 'disallowable' orbital is fundamental. So, why should we not apply this concept to our own particular problem? Indeed, it might also serve as an explanation of why, as many seem to feel, the aerogenous solute (dissolved atmospheric gases), viz. oxygen, nitrogen and carbon dioxide, are not imprinted upon the diluent. We could, of course, state that, in accordance with the propositions of Element XVIII, their presence is insufficient to produce any significant effect. However, there is no evidence that pure potencies of these gases can have any biological action, and thus their existence in potentised form is highly debatable.

Quantity is not quality

For all its virtues, the orbital energy theory, as thus far developed, does not appear to explain satisfactorily the matter of *potency* or 'strength' of a remedy. Neither does it appear to offer an explanation of any differences in therapeutic properties between the centesimal, decimal and LM scales, which do exist. Indeed, a further theoretical argument is required to resolve the basis for these phenomena.

The first point to be made is that *potency* is not just an expression of strength of action. Certainly with regard to the *polychrests* (major remedies of wide therapeutic application), such as Phosphorus and Arsenicum album, there may be manifest considerable qualitative differences in therapeutic effect between the lower and the higher potencies. These differences are often apparent when treating a single individual with different potencies of the same remedy. For example, in an individual sensitive to Arsenicum album, the effects of the 6th centesimal may be quite dissimilar to those of a 10M (10000c). Arsenicum 6c may alleviate a dryness of the skin or mild allergic rhinitis, but the 10M may have profound effects on both the psyche and the general physiology, and is, therefore, said to act *constitutionally.* If this were merely a result of the quantity (that is to say, the number of 'promoted' diluent molecules) of Arsenicum album given, then we should be able to demonstrate that a large material dose of the 6th centesimal has similar effects to those of a small dose of a 10M. In practice, however, this is not the case. On the other hand, we could argue that the dissimilarity of action is more likely based upon the concentration (moles/litre) of the imprinted molecules of diluent. In that case, we should never need serial dilution beyond those points on the various scales (decimal, centesimal, LM) where the original substance is no longer present to any significant degree. Having substantially reduced its concentration by initial serial dilution, thus protecting our patients from any potential toxicity, we could then continue to succuss for a prolonged period. In order then to produce remedies of different qualitative effect, it would only be necessary to dilute the highly-succussed liquid to varying degrees. This, of course, would be much simpler than our normal method of preparation. However, as it turns out, the dilution of a particular potency does not significantly alter its principle therapeutic sphere of action. A remedy that acts constitutionally continues to do so, even after it has been simply diluted to a significant degree. What does alter, however, is its aggressiveness. It is less likely to induce *healing crisis* or *proving symptoms* which may be characteristic of its undiluted form. It might be held that this phenomenon is more likely a true effect of the reduction of material dose (that is to say, the administration of less 'promoted' molecules of diluent), and not one purely dependent upon concentration as such. In fact, as we shall see in Element XXII, there is yet another factor involved in this unusual property of remedies.

The best way of viewing the concept of *potency*, aside from mere numerical expression, is that it tends to define the *range* of action of a remedy. A 10M of Arsenicum album is usually broader in clinical effect than a 6th centesimal in an individual sensitive to its action. There is, as many will be aware, the extremely sensitive subject who experiences almost as broad an action from the 6th centesimal of a particular remedy as he or she does from a 10M. Although these people are not as rare as some might think, their reaction does not destroy the argument. There is, in these cases, still a difference in reactivity between the lower and the higher potencies, but the reactive gap between them has been narrowed.

The concept of *strength* of action with regard to potency, whilst secondary to the idea of therapeutic range, cannot, however, be ignored. With regard to the constitution or psyche, a 50M (50000c) of a particular remedy will more likely hold its effects longer than a 10M; thus prolonging the interval between successive doses. Additionally, in the treatment of some acute diseases, the use of a 30th or 200th centesimal of whatever may be better than that of a 6th, with an appropriate acceleration of the cure.

It is thus apparent that the concept of *potency* has two facets; the major one concerning therapeutic range, and the lesser concerning force or strength of action.

In view of what has been said, we cannot base the differences in action of the potencies of a particular remedy purely upon either the number or the concentration of the imprinted diluent molecules that are administered. We are, therefore, obliged to seek another physical foundation for this phenomenon.

Back into orbit

In unravelling the physical basis for *potency*, we are fortunate in having a few tangible clues.

In Element VIII we noted that the experimental results of various workers have suggested that specific rhythmic vibration patterns do exist in both water and alcohol, and that these patterns do change from potency to potency. The observed frequencies were, in fact, in the kHz range or below; and, assuming these measurements to be correct, we must attempt to explain their origin.

Our first port of call is the *O–H bond* of the *hydroxyl group*. Callinan[8] has indeed suggested that this is capable of storing frequency information. However, in this respect he is referring to a frequency which is characteristic of the individual chemical composition of the solute, rather than of its potency. As we also noted in Element VIII, the idea of solute representation by specific frequency is extremely unlikely, if not impossible. Yet, retaining this speculative variable frequency, whilst rejecting its proposed association, there is still the possibility that O–H bond vibration might, in some way, be connected with the expression of potency. However, the various known frequencies associated with the O–H bond are in the infrared range, which, being in the MHz domain, are considerably greater than those cited previously; and to propose that this bond should acquire a low frequency character, would be to stretch, not only the bond, but also the imagination to the highest degree.

Our next port of call is the *hydrogen bond*. This, however, as has been said, is a most impermanent and volatile structure, with a life expectancy in the order of 10^{-11} to 10^{-10} of a second. If we regard the rate at which it is created and destroyed as its frequency, it is, therefore, even higher than that of the O–H bond, and in the ultraviolet range. A further failure!

Another possible candidate is the additional vibrational mode of a molecule that involves *rotation* about an axis through the centre of its mass. Rotation of diluent molecules is, however, effectively denied by hydrogen bonding between them. Even if it could occur, it would be in the infrared range of frequency expression, and, therefore, again too high. Another non-starter.

A remaining possibility is the occurrence of harmonic, non-thermal *oscillatory motions* of the diluent molecules, and this, indeed might be taken seriously. Such a vibratory phenomenon must be associated with an *electromagnetic field* of like vibrational character. We might then adopt the thesis that there is some degree of interdependence and mutual reinforcement between the field and the diluent. In that way the field becomes an *energising* entity, and not a mere passive product of molecular oscillation. This idea we have met before in the 'goldfish bowl' of Element VII, to which you might wish to refer. It is, as will be apparent, none other than a version of the *dynamic field theories* discussed therein.

We now have a very simple, and superficially plausible, hypothesis. When we succuss, the diluent molecules, in accordance with the principle of 'superradiance' (as discussed in Element VII), are caused to oscillate in harmony with a particular frequency, being supported by the energetic field of their own making. When we succuss again, the oscillatory frequency of both diluent and field increases.

However, it might be held that, when we succuss, the violently applied kinetic energy and the ensuing rupture of the tethering hydrogen bonds, so disorganises the diluent molecules as to send them in many directions, willy-nilly, and destroy their pattern of oscillation, and thus that of their associated field. Upon this basis, it is very difficult to see how there is any cohesive, harmonic and coherent oscillation that can even resurrect itself from such a disarray, let alone gain any increased vibrational status from subsequent and similar events. However, rather as the internal bond vibrations of molecules are preserved during translation and collision, it is more likely that this oscillation of molecules is also similarly maintained under the same circumstances.

Nevertheless, it is still necessary to supply energy in the resting state to the dynamic field and, hence, to its oscillating molecules or ions, in order to extend their activity. In this respect, we must again return to the concept of *energy storage* within the diluent; and, as we shall discover, by means of a simple development of the *orbital energy theory*, the possible nature of the generation and maintenance of potency *per se* may be resolved.

ELEMENT XXII

How to make use of surplus income

In Element XVI we investigated the idea of energy storage upon the lone pair electrons of the oxygen atoms of the diluent hydroxyl groups by means of the adsorption of energetic quanta, termed *orbitons*. These were conceptualised as a genus of *virtual ultraviolet photons,* capable of transference of higher orbital energy information between colliding molecules.

Despite the fact that current *wave mechanics* does not embrace the possibility of such superadded and variable potential energy levels of the electron within a specific orbital, it still remains a viable concept. After all, until the modern physicist is obliged to accept the validity of homoeopathy (and perhaps 'cold fusion'), he will have no need to consider such modification to his existing ideas. Certainly, a science that not only denies the existence of the homoeopathic phenomenon of potentisation, but also, therefore, fails to explain it, is somewhat incomplete and restricted. Anyway, there we present it for them to digest: the notion of different superadded potential energy levels of an electron within its specific orbital, but only under *special circumstances*. In this respect it would appear that an orbital can only be defined as a certain region of space, delineated in relation to the nucleus, in which the electron travels according to the rules of wave mechanics. On the face of it, we can no longer define an orbital in *all* cases in terms of a specific and invariable level of electronic energy, but rather in terms of, what might be called, an energetic *intraorbital ground state*.

However, there is another theoretical approach which may be more acceptable. In accordance with Einstein's concept, the mass of a particle is determined by the sum of its kinetic and potential energies. When a lone pair electron adsorbs an orbiton, its mass, therefore, should increase. Provided it continues to move with the same velocity, this increase in mass leads to a rise in its kinetic energy. So, a rise in both potential and kinetic energy would seem to be consequent upon electronic energetic adsorption. However, if, as a consequence of the adsorption of such a quantum of energy, the velocity of the electron should diminish, then it is possible that the resultant diminution of kinetic energy might balance the increase in potential energy. Thereby, both the total energy and the total mass of the energised electron remain the same, merely at the cost of its velocity. In this way, the sacrosanct energy level of the orbital is preserved.

In order to be promoted, a lone pair electron must accumulate sufficient identical orbitonic quanta. According to the rules, it can only adsorb the quanta of *dissimilar* molecules or ions (which also must be 'allowable'; see Element XIX), thus preventing blocking of the promotive mechanism. These are supplied by collision with either other molecular (or ionic) species, or diluent molecules whose lone pair electrons have been promoted, so making them effectively dissimilar to those of the 'unpromoted' diluent. What is apparent, in the latter case, is that the *molecular orbital theory* (as described in Element XIII) breaks down for diluents other than water. The unified molecular orbital structure of the 'promoted' diluent molecule divides into separate moieties. Taking ethanol ($CH_3.CH_2.OH$) as an example, the promoted lone pair electrons of the hydroxyl group oxygen atom dominate the energetic pattern of that group (OH), and cause it to act as one energetic moiety, whilst the rest of the molecule ($CH_3.CH_2$) acts as another (the results of NMR spectroscopy, as given in Element XI, tend to confirm this view). The 'promoted' hydroxyl group (the *promotable moiety*) functions rather as the solute molecule or ion that has induced its 'promotion', and produces the same energetic species of orbiton upon collision. The remainder of the ethanol molecule (the *unpromotable moiety*, $CH_3.CH_2$) retains the energetic conformation that previously characterised the whole 'unpromoted' molecule, and, as such, cannot be imprinted upon ethanol (in that an energetic molecular species cannot register upon another the same), or indeed upon water (because, in accordance with the principle given in Element XIX, it is 'disallowed'). A similar 'splitting' process can be envisaged to occur with 'promoted' lactose, with similar consequences. In the case of 'promoted' water, however, 'splitting' cannot take place, since the molecule effectively functions as a single, though bifurcate, hydroxyl group.

Those diluent molecules that do not acquire enough of these 'gift tokens' to engender 'promotion', thus effectively have a surplus of potential energy which is, in figurative terms, of little use to them. This energetic state is *metastable,* and energy is slowly and spontaneously shed (without collision) by the loss of orbitonic quanta. As each energetic quantum is shed, so, we may postulate, the velocity of the electron increases, so as to raise its kinetic energy and, therefore, compensate for the loss of potential energy and thus mass. In so doing, the total energy of the electron (the sum of its kinetic and potential energies) and total mass are maintained.

More importantly, from our point of view, the gradual loss of orbitonic quanta from unpromoted lone pair electrons is capable of contributing to the production and maintenance of an electromagnetic *dynamic field* (see Element VII).

It has already been suggested (in Element XVII) that a *promoted* lone pair electron might also be capable of orbitonic storage (within 'allowable' limits). Applying the rule that requires such orbitons to be dissimilar, it follows that they may not store orbitons of the molecule or ion of which they are representative, but only those of other molecular or ionic species, and, more significantly, those characteristic of the diluent itself (including orbitons of the *unpromotable moieties*). However, another rule for the promoted electron is that it cannot be directly transposed to another target orbital by the accumulation of dissimilar orbitons, and, therefore, that *repotentisation* is 'disallowed'; in this way, its position is protected. Any energy thus adsorbed is slowly and spontaneously shed (without collision), and without any change in the total energetic status of the electron. However, the adsorption of such energy (within 'allowable' limits) is advantageous in preserving the promoted electron from rapid decay to a lower orbital, and thus maintains its status of metastability rather than instability. In contrast, according to the rules, the *collision* of a 'promoted' diluent molecule with another molecule always results in the production of orbitons from the promoted electrons which are characteristic of their acquired orbital energies, and not those of dissimilar quanta that have been randomly adsorbed (an unpromoted electron, even though it has adsorbed dissimilar quanta, also behaves similarly in *collision*).

The gradual spontaneous loss of orbitonic quanta from promoted lone pair electrons contributes to the production and support of the electromagnetic field, to which we have referred previously.

The rate of spontaneous dispersion of orbitonic quanta from both the unpromoted and promoted lone pair electrons is dependent upon the amount of potential energy they have stored, and diminishes exponentially with its loss. The rate of metastable loss of orbitonic energy only partially determines the frequency of the dynamic field (for, as we shall see below, successive energy also makes a more direct and important contribution). This frequency is unrelated to the notional ultraviolet frequencies of the shed orbitons, which, in any event, will differ considerably. The rate of spontaneous shedding of surplus orbitons is not affected by the translatory motions of the molecules as such, unless further energisation occurs by forceful collision.

The nature of this field, the frequencies of which probably belong in the kHz range or below, is created by the spontaneous conversion of the orbitonic energy into a lower form (of longer wavelength). Most importantly, the field, its energy, and its frequency are in turn modified, without orbitonic influence, by the more direct conversion of mechanical successive energy into electromagnetic energy (this occurs by the transformation of molecular or ionic translational energy induced by succussion). The energy of this field, in turn, by conversion into kinetic energy, causes the molecules of the diluent to oscillate in harmony and with the same frequency. Since the orbitons which support this process are *virtual particles*, and thus by definition can never be measured or 'seen' except by their resultant actions, we would seem to have created a spontaneous field and set of molecular oscillations that mutually maintain themselves independently of other energetic sources. Although the philosophical reality is somewhat different, in that we have deduced the origin of the field and the oscillations, the scientific, that is to say the *measurable* or *potentially measurable*, aspects must also be allowed to stand. Thus, from such a purely mensurational point of view, we have a group of diluent molecules behaving in an harmonious or 'superradiant' fashion in relation to a mutually supportive electromagnetic field (see Elements VII & X). In scientific terms, the driving force for these physical manifestations, viz. the production of immeasurable orbitons, is committed to the realms of *uncertainty* (see Element X).

Another property of the dynamic field that we might propose is the ability of its frequency (which is the expression of potency) to resist significant reduction by unsuccussed dilution, even to a considerable degree; certainly up to that specified by the LM scale, viz. 1:50000, and probably way beyond. It would be quite logical to think that there must be some dependence of field frequency not only upon its rate of energisation, but also upon the density or concentration of this energy per unit of volume. Therefore, as the vial contents are diluted, so should the dynamic field manifest a proportionately lesser frequency. However, every time a dilution is carried out, even if not followed by traditional succussion, there is, in reality, the induction of a fair degree of molecular agitation. It might be presumed that such is the magnitude of this applied energy of mixing alone, that it more or less maintains the energy of the field. This argument, however, provides only a partial explanation. A greater factor in the phenomenon might concern the state of balance between the energetic density of the dynamic field and the stored energy on the lone pair electrons. There is, if you like, an energetic gradient between them, which causes orbitonic energy to flow from the electrons to the field; rather as the flow of electricity is governed by the *potential difference*. For every small increment of further dilution, there tends to be a small reduction in field density. This, in turn, increases the 'potential difference' between the field and the energised electrons, causing them to release orbitonic energy at a faster rate; and this tends to oppose any reduction of frequency. The drain on electronic stored energy is thus increased, and the life of the preparation shortened. Only succussion or agitation can restore this energy, which, furthermore, is generally increased by them, so that each succussed or agitated serial dilution has a higher frequency than the one that precedes it.

However, there is another factor of great importance in the maintenance of frequency in the face of dilution, and this involves the relationship of the electrodynamic field with the molecules of diluent, whether these be 'promoted' or not. In combination, the field and the molecules constitute a type of *frequency capacitor*. The total energy of this system is determined by the sum of the energy of the field itself (which is related to its frequency) and that of the oscillatory motions of the molecules. Unlike the field, the molecular oscillatory energy is not only determined by frequency, but also by *amplitude* (field and molecular frequency, and molecular oscillatory amplitude are quantised; that is to say, they are discontinuous or 'stepped'). The greater the amplitude of oscillation at a given frequency, the greater will be the kinetic energy (actually, the maximum permissible amplitude must diminish as the frequency increases). As a result of simple dilution, kinetic energy is shed from the oscillating molecules by a reduction in amplitude. This energy is then donated to the dynamic field in the form of electromagnetic energy, in order to maintain its frequency. A certain amount must also be passed to the unpotentised molecules of the fresh diluent, which then vibrate sympathetically within the field. The specific oscillatory frequency and amplitude of the molecules are persistent and biologically coherent even in the face of thermal translation. The reduction of 'aggressiveness' referred to in Element XX in relation to the simple unsuccussed further dilution of remedies, is not, therefore, merely a function of the reduction of imprinted molecular concentration; it is also a function of the reduction in amplitude of molecular oscillation. Once a diluent molecule exhibits maximum amplitude for a given frequency, having gained this by agitation or succussion, it can no longer be accelerated to a higher frequency. In order for this to occur, it must have its amplitude reduced by dilution; whereupon it may be induced to acquire a higher frequency by the application of further mechanical energy. In this way, the diluent molecules control the development of the frequency of the field itself, for they must maintain a state of harmony. This explains the necessity of serial dilution to produce higher and higher field frequencies.

Because the development of frequency by the field-molecular system is limited by the molecules, and because their development of frequency, in turn, is limited by their physical properties (mass, elasticity, etc.), there is a theoretical upper limit to frequency, and thereby potency. There is little point, therefore, in producing potencies in excess of CM (100000c), for there will be but a minute and biologically insignificant gain in frequency. Neither will you be surprised to learn that there is only a marginal therapeutic difference between a 50M (50000c) and a CM potency, even though 50,000 episodes of applied mechanical energy separate them.

Because of this ability of the dynamic field to be maintained, more or less, in the face of unsuccussed dilution, the veterinary homoeopathist can dump but a small quantity of liquid potency into a relatively vast quantity of cattle drinking-water, and still be assured that the potency of the remedy (and, therefore, its speed or range of action) will be, more or less, preserved.

Two additional points are now worthy of further discussion. The first concerns the processing of orbitons, which in terms of their energetic species would be normally 'allowable', but arrive at their target unpromoted diluent lone pair electron, only to find that it is saturated with orbitonic quanta, and cannot store any more. Should it combine with its fellows to produce promotion, then it will be adsorbed. Yet, should there be an insufficient number of these, would it be rejected? Would there be, in effect, a block to the promotional system? The answer is that it would not necessarily be rejected; for the electron can select which orbiton to reject only upon a random basis. In such a manner, the surplus orbiton may escape rejection, and the process of random adsorption of orbitons is not impeded (a similar random rejection process may be postulated with regard to the adsorption of orbitons by energetically saturated promoted electrons).

The second point concerns the problem of the 'inadsorbable' orbiton. This, in fact, arises as a result of various types of collision. For example, the collision of a solute molecule (or ion) with a solute molecule (or ion), of different or identical species; or that of an unpromotable moiety with another unpromotable moiety. Inadsorption may be also consequent upon the random rejection process described above with regard to energetically saturated diluent lone pair electrons (where the incoming orbiton is randomly rejected). All of these inadsorbable orbitons may contribute, upon rejection, to the collective energy of the electromagnetic dynamic field, described previously.

If left in a totally undisturbed state, a liquid potency will exponentially lose energy, which is dispersed as heat. The frequency of the dynamic field will decline together with that of the diluent molecules, which will become 'depromoted'. The occasional agitation, as I have remarked, will oppose this decay. However, when we dispense our remedies as impregnated solids (pilules, tablets, granules, etc.), the energised molecules contained therein cannot be agitated to any degree sufficient to protect them from energetic decay, and thus their life expectancy is much shorter.

Commercial brewing and pickling

It should be now apparent that the whole process of homoeopathic potentisation may be regarded as the property of one basic particle, the electron; and this property is no more complex than its potential to accept or reject certain forms of additional energy (orbitonic quanta). This propensity is totally determined by its specific orbital energy, and, should the electron switch to another orbital, so will it change; for only particular species of orbitonic quanta are compatible with any given level of orbital energy. Terms, such as 'disallowed' and 'allowable' are purely metaphoric caricatures used to illustrate specific energetic constraints, and should not be taken to imply that the electron has any choice in what it does. Orbitonic quanta are either compatible with the electron in its level of orbital energisation, and potentially adsorbable, or they are incompatible, and consequentially inadsorbable. The electron has no choice in a matter which is entirely decided by the basic rules of Nature; and, even when saturated, orbitonic quanta are solely dispersed by random process, and without intent. So, similarly, is energy shed in the process of metastable decay.

Having reduced homoeopathic potentisation to a phenomenon so simple in its basis (yet, complex in its ramifications), we are now ready to consider the cardinal physical differences between the decimal, centesimal and LM scales.

The first and obvious difference relates to the presence or absence of intended solute molecules in the lower potencies. This is purely related to the degree of dilution, and thus this solute persists furthest into the decimal series of potencies. Up to 11x or 6c, there are still sufficient molecules of the intended solute to contribute towards the biological action of the remedy; although, this depends to a great degree upon the bioactivity of the solute, and is, therefore, more relevant to highly toxic substances, such as arsenious oxide. Additionally, as the numerical limits of significance are approached, that contribution becomes negligible. With regard to the LM scale, even LM1 contains an insignificant number of such bioactive molecules.

Since many substances must be triturated with lactose to the level of 3c or 6x before being dissolved in ethanol-water, it follows that lactose is always present in the initial liquid potencies prepared from this material, starting with 7x, 4c and LM1. This presence, however, which obviously fades with progressive dilution, seems to have no effect whatsoever on the properties of the remedy. This is particularly surprising in view of the fact that lactose is the most dominant component of the intended solute. Fortunately, the *exclusion principle*, that denies the representation of certain molecules within the diluent, comes to our aid (see Element XIX). Lactose cannot be energetically impressed upon either ethanol or water, and vice versa.

The next point with which we should familiarise ourselves is the notion of *solute inhibition* (see also Element XXVI for other comments upon this matter). Have you ever wondered why sea-water is virtually unpotentised? Surely, with all that common salt, and the crashing of the waves on the sea shore, it must be loaded with high potency Sodium chloride, and have internal properties akin to those of Natrum muriaticum (which is prepared from rock-salt). Never another headache, perhaps? Never another cold-sore? No, Sir! No such benefit at all.

Some might argue that the sunlight destroys the potency; but sea-water swallowed in a midnight swim is just as unpleasant and unbeneficial as that imbibed in the day. Indeed, internally administered sea-water has no discernible therapeutic properties whatsoever. It might be argued that potentised molecules of water are adsorbed by dispersed organic material. And I can see no reason to disagree with this idea in principle; but why should this be to such a degree that the sea-water is rendered virtually inert? After all, when the vet dumps small amounts of liquid potency into a cattle trough or whatever, he still expects his remedy to work, even with all the organic matter to be found therein, and hence is not surprised when it does.

The key to the mystery probably lies in the electrical properties of ions and molecules. The major components of most solutes are ions or polar molecules. Water molecules are also polar, and, as discussed in Element VI, form 'protective' *hydration shells* that enshroud or encapsulate the ions or polar molecules. Ethanol, which is similarly polar, has a similar capacity. The attraction of the diluent molecules to an ion is quite strong, since the ion carries at least one full unit of electric charge; whereas the polar molecule is quite weakly charged, and the attraction, therefore, more feeble. Certainly with regard to ions, the adherent shell of diluent bars many of them from direct collision with any diluent molecules, during both agitation and succussion. The shell around a polar molecule is more fragile, and more readily fragmented. However, a small proportion of ions, and a greater percentage of polar solute molecules, will be freed by succussion, and potentisation will proceed on this basis. As 'promoted' diluent molecules are produced in greater amounts by serial dilution and succussion, effectively replacing the encapsulated solute ions and molecules, the whole process of potentisation proceeds with greater rapidity, since these imprinted molecules are not subject to encapsulation. We may now make certain deductions:

(1) Triturated materials are not subject to diluent encapsulation. Therefore, potentisation proceeds faster with this method. Thus, triturated Natrum muriaticum 6x should be more biologically active than Natrum muriaticum 6x developed only in weak ethanol-water [see also (5) below].

(2) Non-ionic, non-polar molecules, such as sulphur (S_8), are imprinted readily upon the diluent; in that they are only very weakly electrically charged in solution, and water molecules so attracted to them are easily dislodged by agitation or succussion. Sulphur is well-known for its powerful bioactivity in low potencies, part of which may be accounted for by its diminutive charge.

(3) Organic substances, most of which are polar, are more readily potentised than ions, since their encapsulating shells are more fragile. They will, therefore, have a more dominant expression in the diluent than any ions with which they are mixed, and quite out of proportion to their relative molar concentration.

(4) The strength of the electrostatic adherence of the encapsulating diluent shell is determined by the numerical value of the charge of the ion (but not by its polarity). An ion of double charge, such as SO_4^{2-}, is more attractive of diluent molecules than an ion of single charge, be it either positive or negative. This significantly reduces its ability to collide freely with diluent molecules, and thus it has a quantitatively lesser imprint than an ion of single charge present in equimolar concentration.

(5) The addition of ethanol to water to form the diluent may be advantageous, in that ethanol may form mixed shells with water, somewhat weaker than those of water alone.

(6) With regard to mother tinctures of plant materials, where their therapeutically important constituents are mainly polar organic

molecules, it is advantageous for them to be as concentrated as possible. In this way, the representation of any dissolved contaminant ions, from rain-water or soil on their exterior, or contained within the diluent, will be minimised. At the same time, however, the ionic constituents of the plant (essentially, its minerals) will suffer similarly, but these are usually of lesser therapeutic importance. Additionally, a high initial concentration favours the successive development of imprinted molecules.

(7) The more powerful the stroke of succussion, the more likely the encapsulating diluent shells around the ions will be broken, which enhances their ability to imprint the diluent.

From these various inferences, you may now realise that the simplified view of molecular collision, given in Element XVIII, is somewhat inaccurate, unless we place upon it certain constraints. The illustration of probabilities only retains its mathematical validity if the two solute particles be either ions of equal charge or molecules of similar polar strength. This, however, does not destroy the argument concerning the selective representation of solute molecules, but merely serves to modify it favourably and constructively.

Having disposed of these basic points, in order to consider the cardinal physical differences between the three major scales, we must be conversant with the following principles and their consequences; bearing in mind that pure dilution strictly cannot occur, since some agitation of the preparation must always be associated with it:

(1) Dilution itself reduces the concentration of 'promoted' diluent molecules. This reduction is theoretically proportional to the degree of dilution. Hence, for each phase of serial dilution, it should be 90% on the decimal scale, 99% on the centesimal and 99.998% on the LM. In reality, the agitation consequent upon mixing, by producing 'promoted' molecules, reduces these figures to a degree.

(2) Dilution (within limits) causes little or no change in dynamic field frequency, and thus potency. Certainly, if we dumped 10ml of liquid potency into Lake Ontario, this would not be so! However, the precise limit will remain unknown, until biological experiments are performed (such as those of the Benveniste[9] type) to establish its value.

(3) Dilution (again, within limits) favours the increase in frequency (and thus potency), if followed by significant agitation or succussion.

(4) Succussion increases the number of 'promoted' molecules of diluent.

(5) Succussion increases field frequency (and thus potency). However,

as we discussed in Element XXII, blocking of this process will occur when the diluent molecules reach maximum oscillatory amplitude. Dilution is then a prerequisite for any further increase in quantised frequency. Alternatively, if we had the patience, we could leave the preparation to age, and by the metastable loss of energy, the amplitude would decrease. Left too long, however, the molecules (and dynamic field) would fall to a lower frequency, initially at maximum amplitude for that frequency, and we would have missed the boat again.

It follows from these various points, given above and discussed previously, that there must be considerable physical differences between the three major scales of serial dilution. However, except in the vaguest terms, is it possible to infer what these might be without the development of a *mathematical model* to assist us. This, indeed, will be the subject of Element XXIV.

It should now be apparent that, when we administer a remedy, it is not simply a matter of delivering imprinted diluent molecules. At the same time, we are supplying a dynamic field (containing oscillating molecules), which considerably alters the biological reaction. When we come to consider variations in bioactivity of a particular remedy in different potencies, aside from issues of subject sensitivity, we may be forced to unravel the significance of such matters as molecular concentration, total dosage, frequency and amplitude.

One final point is worth making concerning energisation of the diluent. More kinetic energy is required to produce an orbiton from an element of higher outermost orbital energy, than one with a lower energetic configuration; and similarly with regard to their representative diluent molecules. At that rate, all things being equal (which, in the real World, they are generally not), copper should be more difficult to potentise than sulphur. A more forceful collision is required for the copper molecule than the sulphur. This is, perhaps, another element of persuasion in advocating the successive blow in preference to simple agitation of the liquid potency.

Having deliberated, cogitated, and, hopefully not regurgitated, we are now ready to move on to some homoeopathic mathematics.

The day of reckoning is nigh

Whereas the manner of serial dilution itself has been highly standardised into three scales (decimal, centesimal and LM), that of succussion has not. This diversity of technique has, in fact, stemmed from an inability to comprehend the processes involved in potentisation. As you will now be aware, variations in successive technique are responsible for significant differences in the physical, and hence therapeutic, properties of a remedy. The two cardinal parameters are the *total energy* delivered at each phase of serial dilution, and the *rate* of its delivery. The same principles govern trituration.

Two other factors, which may be of some importance, are *temperature* and *atmospheric pressure*. One of the functions of succussion is to rupture the hydrogen bonds which link the diluent molecules into polymeric groups, thus allowing free collision to occur. This, of course, requires a proportion of successive energy. The density or concentration of hydrogen bonds varies as to the temperature of the diluent and the ambient barometric pressure. The pressure itself is also related partially to *altitude*. The greater the amount of energy devoted to hydrogen bond dissolution, the less there is available for inducing molecular collision. Potentisation would thus be more effective in an overheated laboratory, during stormy weather, in the Swiss Alps, than in an unheated room, during fine and cold weather, in the Netherlands. These factors, which are essentially irrelevant to trituration, may be of some importance when considering standardisation of liquid phase technique; but the magnitude of their effect is yet to be ascertained.

As it is our intention to produce some mathematical structure for comparing the three standard scales in terms of potency and imprinted molecular concentration, we must be aware of the diversity of successive technique. For our purposes, we must assume that each succussion, which normally consists of a shake followed by a blow, has been standardised in terms of total kinetic energy and the rate at which it is applied (this rate will, of course, be less during the 'shake' than during the 'blow'). Essentially, therefore, we are restricted to comparing preparations of pharmacies who succuss in the same classical way (less aggressive methods, where agitation is used rather than classical succussion, will produce less molecular 'promotion' and lesser development of dynamic field frequency; forceful succussion with a mechanical device will, of course, have the opposite effect). We are not, however, constrained by the actual *number* of succussions delivered at each phase of serial dilution, for this factor can be allowed for in the mathematics. As the ambient temperature is more or less the same in most pharmacies, we can reasonably ignore its influence. However, the same cannot be said for the atmospheric pressure, which varies according to meteorological conditions and altitude; but, since we have no reason to assume that it is of major significance, we shall just plain ignore it.

The object of our mathematics is to produce numerical expressions which characterise imprinted ('promoted') molecular concentration and dynamic field frequency (and thus, potency), so that we may compare their expression through the three major scales of potentisation (the mathematical expression of potency itself is fully discussed in Element XXVI). It also should allow us to predict the potential physical properties of other scales of potentisation not yet conceived.

Since, in this Element of the text, we are concerned with the effects of succussion, as opposed to trituration, we shall restrict our attention to liquid phase potentisation. Lactose itself, triturations with this substance, and liquid phase preparations derived therefrom are discussed more fully in Element XXV (including a detailed discussion of the LM scale, which always begins with a 3c trituration).

As we have deduced previously, the initial stages of liquid phase potentisation may develop different substances to different degrees, so that ionic materials are initially less easily potentised than those which are polar or minimally charged. Although this is of some importance, we may ignore it for the purposes of creating numerical expressions, whose significance lies more in their ability to allow comparison between different methods of serial potentisation, than being absolutely correct in their own right.

For each stage of liquid phase serial dilution, irrespective of scale, the dilution factor D is related to the succussion factor Z in the following way:

$$Z/D > 1$$

The dilution factor D is the reciprocal of the dilution. So, for the centesimal scale, the dilution at each stage is $1/100$, and the dilution factor

D is thus 100. The succussion factor Z is one plus the number of moles of imprinted diluent molecules (ethanol and water) produced from one mole of intended solute, imprinted ethanol or water molecules, 'promoted' lactose moieties, or mixtures of these (or, if you like, one plus the notional number of imprinted molecules produced from one molecule or ion of intended solute, one imprinted ethanol or water molecule, or one imprinted lactose hydroxyl group). For convenience, we shall ignore the presence (and any imprinting effects) of diluent impurities.

How can we justify this expression? Very simply! If

$$Z/D < 1,$$

then, as serial dilution progressed, all molecules, including imprinted ones, would progressively disappear from the preparation, and ultimately there would be no remedy!

Of course,

$$Z/D = 1$$

is a possibility, but would not allow any development of the remedy, in that the number of 'medicinal entities' would always remain the same (by 'medicinal entities', I collectively refer to any residual intended solute molecules or ions, the imprinted ethanol and water molecules, and, where imprinted lactose is present, as is always the case in the lower LM dilutions, the 'promoted' lactose hydroxyl groups).

Going further, if Z were much greater than D, then all the lower potencies associated with the particular method under consideration would be rapidly saturated with imprinted molecules. This would seem to be inconsistent with Hahnemann's intentions, so we won't allow it to happen. Z/D is limited to being only slightly greater than 1 for 2 succussions on the centesimal scale (Hahnemann's original recommended number of succussions) and 100 succussions on the LM scale.

Z is actually an exponential function of the number of succussions applied after each stage of serial dilution. This is simply because imprinting gathers 'momentum' as more imprinted molecules become available for collision:

$$Z = ab^s,$$

where a and b are constants, irrespective of scale of dilution, and s is the number of succussions. In fact, a is chosen to be 100 and b, 1.065, so that

$$Z = 100 \times 1.065^s,$$

which satisfies our criteria for the development of imprinted diluent molecules.

The expression Z/D may now be defined for different scales of dilution, in the order of decimal, centesimal and LM:

$$100(1.065^s)/10$$
$$100(1.065^s)/100$$
$$100(1.065^s)/50000$$

We shall now solve these expressions, where s is 10 (as commonly used) for the decimal scale, 2 (Hahnemann's original) for the centesimal and 100 (which have always been used) for the LM. Given in order:

$$100(1.065^{10})/10 = 18.771$$
$$100(1.065^2)/100 = 1.134$$
$$100(1.065^{100})/50000 = 1.086$$

This means that, for each stage of serial potentisation, 1 mole of medicinal entities becomes 1.086 moles for LM preparations, 1.134 moles for classical centesimals, and a most aggressive 18.771 moles for the post-Hahnemannian decimals.

Let us now see what happens when we introduce 10 and 20 successions respectively, with regard to a centesimal preparation; 10 being common modern practice, and 20 being advocated by some:

$$100(1.065^{10})/100 = 1.877$$
$$100(1.065^{20})/100 = 3.524$$

So, 10 successions, contrary to what you might think, are not five times as effective as 2. In fact, as it turns out, the increase in effect is fairly modest. 20, however, is going some. For those who like to succuss the guts out of a liquid potency, consider the case where s is 100 for the centesimal scale:

$$100(1.065^{100})/100 = 543.201$$

Horrific, is it not, for the cause of gentle development of medicinal expression?

So far we have considered the mathematics of only a single stage of serial potentisation. What we need to know is how we may compute the effects of a series. In order to do that, we must multiply the Z/D factors of the various phases of that series. Assuming that our dilutions are of an equal degree at each stage, and our number of successions always the same, for both the decimal and centesimal scales, the expression

$$(Z/D)^t$$

gives us the result of t stages of liquid potentisation; t having the same value as the numerical potency (potency number) N for preparations prepared *ab initio* (1c, 1x or LM1) in the liquid phase.

This may be expanded to

$$[100(1.065)^s/D]^t$$

As we have deduced, the expression Z/D has the value of 1.134 for classical centesimal potencies, where 2 succussions have been employed for each stage. Let us, therefore, calculate the values of $(Z/D)^t$ for various centesimal potencies, where they have been prepared throughout only in the liquid phase:

[1c] $1.134^1 = 1.134$
[2c] $1.134^2 = 1.286$
[3c] $1.134^3 = 1.458$
[4c] $1.134^4 = 1.654$
[6c] $1.134^6 = 2.127$
[9c] $1.134^9 = 3.101$
[12c] $1.134^{12} = 4.522$
[30c] $1.134^{30} = 43.490$
[36c] $1.134^{36} = 92.485$
[37c] $1.134^{37} = 104.878$
[200c] $1.134^{200} = 8.368 \times 10^{10}$
[423c] $1.134^{423} = 1.263 \times 10^{23}$
[1M] $1.134^{1000} = 4.103 \times 10^{54}$

Certain interesting points arise out of these calculations. First of all, let us suppose that the intended solute is an hypothetical liquid of similar molecular weight to water, and with similar volumetric properties. In this case, we will only consider water as the diluent. It follows that, at the first centesimal dilution, the molar ratio will be 1 mole of intended solute to 99 moles of diluent. In other words, 1 molecule of our solute to every 99 of water. As potentisation proceeds up the scale, the total number of medicinal molecules (intended solute plus imprinted molecules) increases, whereas the proportion of solute molecules themselves diminishes. When the expression $(Z/D)^t$ becomes 100, then the preparation is completely composed of imprinted molecules. As you can see from the figures given above, this occurs by 37c. All numerical potencies below this are unsaturated, and all above are fully saturated, with no further 'promotion' possible.

At the other extreme, let us consider a case of a weak aqueous extract of a particular substance which contains only 100 solute molecules per 3.6ml (3.6ml = 100 'standard' drops). At the first centesimal dilution, there will be 1 molecule contained in 3.6ml of water (having selected this as our sole diluent). 3.6ml of water contains approximately 1.205×10^{23} molecules available for 'promotion'. According to our calculations given above for $(Z/D)^t$, saturation will thus occur by 423c, where our original one molecule has 'transformed' the entirety of the diluent. Such a theoretical numerical potency (in this case, 423c) we may term the *maximum saturation point*, since saturation must occur at or below this level.

It follows from these rather extreme, but purposeful, examples that the stage of numerical potency at which the diluent becomes saturated is very much dependent upon the initial molar concentration of the intended solute, as is the 'rate' at which imprinting occurs through the potencies. Concentrated mother tinctures produce saturation at lower levels of numerical potency than their weaker brethren. Generally speaking, this higher concentration is advantageous in the lower potencies, and less so in the higher.

Let us now calculate $(Z/D)^t$ for some 'modern' centesimals, prepared throughout in the liquid phase, with 10 successions per dilution, where Z/D is 1.877 as calculated previously:

$$[6c] \ 1.877^6 = 43.731$$
$$[7c] \ 1.877^7 = 82.082$$
$$[8c] \ 1.877^8 = 154.069$$
$$[85c] \ 1.877^{85} = 1.756 \times 10^{23}$$

This means that, irrespective of initial solute concentration, saturation must occur by 85c where the diluent is water alone.

We shall now see how the addition of ethanol influences the number of molecules available for 'promotion'. '95% alcohol' is actually a misnomer, since it may contain from 94.7 to 95.2% ethanol by volume (mean: 94.95%). By weight, it contains 92.0 to 92.7% of ethanol; but, for our purposes, we shall assume this percentage to be the mean, viz. 92.35%. The proportion of water by weight is thus 7.65%. The *relative molecular mass* of water is 18, and that of ethanol is 46. 1g of pure ethanol contains approximately 1.309×10^{22} molecules, whereas 1g of water contains 3.346×10^{22} (these figures are obtained by dividing the *Avogadro constant*, approximately 6.023×10^{23}, by the relative molecular mass of each substance). Therefore, in 100g of '95% alcohol', we have $92.35 \times 1.309 \times 10^{22}$ $(=1.209 \times 10^{24})$ molecules of ethanol, and $7.65 \times 3.346 \times 10^{22}$ $(=2.560 \times 10^{23})$ molecules of water. The mean *specific gravity* $(20°/20°)$ of '95% alcohol' is 0.8129; so that 100g has a volume of $100/0.8129=123$ml. We can now calculate the number of molecules of ethanol and water in 3.6ml. There are

3.6×1.209×10²⁴/123 (=3.539×10²²) molecules of ethanol, and 3.6×2.560×10²³/123 (=7.493×10²¹) molecules of water in this volume. The total number of diluent molecules available for 'promotion' is, therefore, 4.288×10²². Compared with a diluent of water alone, which contains 1.205×10²³ molecules per 3.6ml, this is actually just under one third of the molecular number. Hence, a liquid potency in '95% alcohol', when saturated with imprinted molecules, contains less than one third of the molecular 'information' of one composed solely of water. Moreover, saturation must occur earlier. However, this effect itself is not as dramatic as one might think. For example, with regard to a classical centesimal scale, using 2 succussions per serial dilution, the maximum potency for saturation to occur is 415c, where $(Z/D)^t = 4.618×10^{22}$, instead of 423c for water alone. For a modern centesimal scale, with 10 succussions per serial dilution, the maximum saturation point or level changes from 85c to 83c. Obviously, lesser concentrations of ethanol will exert smaller effects on both the number of available molecules for imprinting and the maximum potency level at which saturation occurs.

Let us now calculate $(Z/D)^t$ values for some decimals, prepared throughout in the liquid phase, with 10 succussions per serial dilution:

$$[1x] \; 18.771^1 = 18.771$$
$$[3x] \; 18.771^3 = 6613.970$$
$$[6x] \; 18.771^6 = 43.744×10^6$$
$$[8x] \; 18.771^8 = 1.541×10^{10}$$
$$[12x] \; 18.771^{12} = 1.914×10^{15}$$
$$[15x] \; 18.771^{15} = 1.266×10^{19}$$
$$[18x] \; 18.771^{18} = 8.371×10^{22}$$
$$[19x] \; 18.771^{19} = 1.571×10^{24}$$

In this case, therefore, 18x is the maximum saturation point for '95% alcohol', and 19x is that for pure water.

Enough of these! On to the LMs and some pertinent comments concerning trituration...

A treatise upon mixed marriages

The *LM scale*[4,16] is rather a special case, since it is actually a composite of two different scales of serial potentisation. Rather perversely, it begins with thorough centesimal triturations in lactose, the third being used to prepare LM1. From LM1 onwards, however, it goes 'straight', with serial dilutions of 1 in 50,000 in the liquid phase and 100 succussions per stage.

It is customary to believe that Hahnemann chose the 3rd centesimal trituration as the base for the LM scale because, at this level of dilution, all substances are soluble in ethanol-water (note that lactose itself is virtually insoluble in strong alcohol). However, with regard to soluble substances (e.g. alcoholic plant extracts), he makes no suggestion that the stage of trituration may be circumvented and that the 3rd centesimal in liquid phase is an acceptable alternative. Mother tinctures of plants are discarded in favour of triturations of the fresh plant material[16]. One of the intentions might be to potentise the more insoluble elements of the plant, which are, of course, only present minimally in the filtered mother tincture. Also, trituration develops imprinting more efficiently than liquid phase technique. In the first place, the encapsulation of ions (and, to some degree, polar molecules) by the diluent is avoided (see Element XXIII). In the second, the whole process is more vigorous and prolonged; both the rate of application of kinetic energy and the total amount delivered are vastly greater. Hahnemann, in fact, advises us to triturate (which involves both grinding and scraping) for one full hour per dilution in lactose[16]. Our conclusion might well be that the lactose molecules are imprinted virtually in their entirety by the end of third centesimal phase of trituration.

At the conclusion of third centesimal trituration, we have 1 part by weight of the original material to 999999 parts by weight of lactose. Let us assume, by way of example, that the original substance or material is mercury (Hg), which will yield the remedy Mercurius vivus. The relative atomic mass of mercury is 201, and the relative molecular mass of lactose is 342. 1g of mercury contains $6.023 \times 10^{23}/201$ ($=2.997 \times 10^{21}$) atoms, and 999999g of lactose contains $6.023 \times 10^{23} \times 999999/342$ ($=1.761 \times 10^{27}$) molecules. However, each lactose molecule has eight *promotable moieties* (hydroxyl groups), and thus, at saturation, each molecule can represent eight atoms of mercury. Therefore, the total number of medicinal entities (i.e. 'promoted' lactose moieties and mercury atoms) in 1×10^{6}g of the 3c trituration is:

$$(2.997 \times 10^{21}) + (8 \times 1.761 \times 10^{27}) = 1.409 \times 10^{28},$$

assuming saturation. Of this number, 99.986% are 'promoted' lactose moieties.

0.06g of the third centesimal trituration is dissolved in 30ml (500 drops) of 20% ethanol, in order to yield a dilution of 1:500 w/v. The final dilution to 1:50000 is then carried out with 1 drop of the 1:500 preparation and 99 drops of 95% alcohol, which, after 100 successions, becomes LM1. Each drop of the 1:500 dilution contains 0.06/500g of the 3c trituration, or the following presuccussive number of medicinal entities (ignoring, for simplicity, any colloidal aggregation of mercury atoms into larger particles):

$$(1.409 \times 10^{28} \times 0.06)/(10^{6} \times 500) = 1.691 \times 10^{18},$$

of which, almost all are promotable lactose moieties. This is the number then contained before succussion in 100 drops of what is virtually 95% ethanol, or 3.6ml (the drops are smaller than those of 20% alcohol because of surface tension differences).

Referring to Element XXIV, you will see that the expression Z/D for the standard LM scale (at 100 successions per dilution) is 1.086. This must be applied to each postsuccussive stage of potentisation, in order to calculate the number of medicinal entities; by which term is meant the totality of intended solute molecules, atoms or ions, and 'promoted' lactose, ethanol and water moieties. In this respect, let us consider the expression $m(Z/D)^{t}$, where, for the LM scale, t has the same value as the numerical potency (potency number) N, and where m is the number of presuccussive medicinal entities. Expressed as $(Z/D)^{t} \times (m)$, in the case of Mercurius vivus, its value for 3.6ml becomes:

$$1.086^{1}(1.691 \times 10^{18}) = 1.836 \times 10^{18},$$

which is the number of postsuccussive medicinal entities for this level of potentisation.

The values for further 1:50000 LM preparations are simply calculated as follows:

$$[LM2] \ 1.086^2(1.691\times10^{18}) = 1.994\times10^{18}$$
$$[LM3] \ 1.086^3(1.691\times10^{18}) = 2.166\times10^{18}$$
$$[LM41] \ 1.086^4(1.691\times10^{18}) = 2.352\times10^{18}$$
$$[LM6] \ 1.086^6(1.691\times10^{18}) = 2.774\times10^{18}$$
$$[LM12] \ 1.086^{12}(1.691\times10^{18}) = 4.548\times10^{18}$$
$$[LM30] \ 1.086^{30}(1.691\times10^{18}) = 2.009\times10^{19}$$

LM30 is, in actual practice, as high as most would need to go. Even at this level, bearing in mind that there are approximately 4.288×10^{22} 'promotable' ethanol and water molecules in 3.6ml of 95% ethanol, the preparation is not fully saturated (all traces of the original lactose and mercury have disappeared by LM5). Indeed, there are still about 99.95% of the diluent molecules left available for imprinting.

In contrast, let us consider a 'modern' liquid 4th centesimal (10 succussions per dilution) prepared from the same 3rd centesimal trituration of Mercurius vivus, with 0.036g of the triturated material being dissolved in 3.6ml of weak ethanol (giving a dilution of 1:100 w/v). The presuccussive medicinal entity presence at the 4th centesimal dilution is given by:

$$(0.036\times1.409\times10^{28})/10^6 = 5.072\times10^{20}$$

Since Z/D for this scale is 1.877, the postsuccussive number becomes:

$$1.877^1(5.072\times10^{20}) = 9.520\times10^{20}$$

You will note that the number 1.877 is to the power of 1, not 4; since the Z/D power factor t only applies to liquid preparations, of which 4c is the first such in this series. Here, $t = N - 3$, where N is the numerical potency.

For some further 'modern' centesimal dilutions, the postsuccussive medicinal entity numbers are:

$$[10c] \ 1.877^7(5.07\times10^{20}) = 4.163\times10^{22}$$
$$[11c] \ 1.877^8(5.07\times10^{20}) = 7.814\times10^{22}$$

It follows that, if potentisation were to continue in 95% alcohol after 4c, saturation would occur at 11c (where the medicinal entity number is $> 4.288\times10^{22}$).

Initially insoluble substances may also be prepared by trituration with lactose on the decimal scale up to 6x, after which they become soluble in ethanol-water. At this level, as with the third centesimal trituration, we might assume full imprinting (that is to say, saturation) of the lactose. Calculations may proceed upon similar lines to those of the centesimal examples. The initial concentration of the lactose-mercury trituration for 7x will be 0.36g per 3.6ml (a dilution of 1:10 w/v). The presuccussive medicinal entity number here is 5.072×10^{21} (10 times the figure for 4c). Since Z/D for this scale (at 10 successions per dilution) is 18.771 (and bearing in mind, in this case, that t = N − 6), the postsuccussive number is:

$$18.771^1(5.072 \times 10^{21}) = 9.521 \times 10^{22}$$

For 8x, the figure becomes:

$$18.771^2(5.072 \times 10^{21}) = 1.787 \times 10^{24}$$

This means that, irrespective of ethanol concentration (even if quite low), saturation must occur by 8x.

Even if we use original substances other than mercury, the above calculations are very similar, since 'promoted' lactose hydroxyl groups are always by far the more dominant medicinal entities at LM1, 4c and 7x; and their ('molar') presence virtually constant and readily calculable. So, even for plant material, the percentage of water which it contains as opposed to medicinal molecules is virtually irrelevant to the computation. This contrasts significantly with the pure liquid phase decimal and centesimal scales, where the initial concentration of the mother tincture very much determines the progression of imprinting as the scale is ascended, and, therefore, the saturation level. The LM and the initially triturated centesimal and decimal scales acquire this consistency by the use of lactose as an intermediary, which is probably fully saturated by the level of 3c or 6x. Molecule for molecule, lactose has eight times the capacity of either ethanol or water for informational storage, in view of its eight promotable moieties (hydroxyl groups). Moreover, each lactose moiety is independent in its capacity for solute representation; and thus, at least theoretically, a single lactose molecule could represent eight different molecules or ions, depending on appropriate collision.

We may make now some general formulations concerning the value of $m(Z/D)^t$ with regard to preparations initially triturated in lactose, where t = N − j (j being an integer of 3 or 6, or zero, according to scale). Given in order of decimal (10 successions [s] per dilution), centesimal (10 successions [s] per dilution), centesimal (2 successions [s] per dilution), LM (100 successions [s] per dilution):

$$18.771^{N-6}(5.072\times10^{21}) \quad [\text{x}, \text{s}=10]$$
$$1.877^{N-3}(5.072\times10^{20}) \quad [\text{c}, \text{s}=10]$$
$$1.134^{N-3}(5.072\times10^{20}) \quad [\text{c}, \text{s}=2]$$
$$1.086^{N}(1.691\times10^{18}) \quad [\text{LM}, \text{s}=100]$$

There is, however, one minor peculiarity of the LM scale which we have so far omitted to discuss. Serial LM dilutions are not carried out beyond LM1 by the mixing of 1 drop of the lower potency with diluent, but by taking 1/500th of a drop for subsequent dilution. This is effected by dispersing 1 drop of the lower potency in 500 small granules (100 of which weigh 0.06g), and using 1 such granule dissolved in 1 drop of water to 99 drops of 95% alcohol to achieve a dilution of 1:50000. This is to reduce the wastage of alcohol, and to produce a lesser volume (3.6ml) which is more easily succussed. These granules are classically composed of cane sugar (sucrose) and starch (polymeric glucose). The weight of each granule is only 0.0006g. It must be assumed that, rather like lactose, they are unimprintable upon both ethanol and water. It is also feasible that, as carbohydrates containing multiple hydroxyl groups, they are similarly capable of 'promotion'. However, unlike the triturated lactose employed as the base for the LM scale, each fresh granule is merely impregnated with imprinted diluent and not potentised by this action alone. The actual contribution of each tiny granule itself to the molecular promotional characteristics of each serial dilution is sufficiently small for it to be essentially ignored.

Lastly, let us calculate some $m(Z/D)^t$ values for some classical liquid centesimals derived from 3c triturations and prepared with only 2 succussions per dilution:

$$[6\text{c}] \; 1.134^3(5.072\times10^{20}) = 7.396\times10^{20}$$
$$[30\text{c}] \; 1.134^{27}(5.072\times10^{20}) = 1.513\times10^{22}$$
$$[39\text{c}] \; 1.134^{36}(5.072\times10^{20}) = 4.691\times10^{22}$$

Molecular 'promotion' consequent upon the classical centesimal scale for initially insoluble substances is greater and progresses more rapidly than that of the LM; this being a result of both its higher initial concentration of triturated lactose and the larger Z/D factor.

Sounds that may fall upon deaf ears

It is quite obvious to the homoeopathist that the induction of a chemical imprint upon the diluent cannot be the sole product of potentisation. We cannot ascribe the varying actions of a particular remedy, in a certain individual, entirely to the material dose or its imprinted molecular concentration. This brings us to the matter of *potency* or *frequency,* which latter has been confused by many with the inductive chemical imprint itself; a fact that I have refuted, and in some detail previously.

An imprinted molecule of ethanol or water generates its biological effect in part by possessing an oscillatory frequency with a particular amplitude. These factors serve to modify the consequences of its electronic mimicry. They are, however, unlike the latter, exhibited only by liquids. Triturated lactose is incapable of such oscillatory activity in the powder state, and, even when dissolved in ethanol-water, its great molecular size and solid nature must prohibit it from coherent oscillation. The same must be said for any other solid substances, such as sucrose, which possess theoretically promotable moieties (hydroxyl groups). However, this does not prohibit such substances from storing liquid potencies and preserving their dynamic fields and liquid molecular oscillations. Hence, they are valuable media for the storage and administration of remedies in the form of granules, powders, tablets and pilules. They do, nevertheless, prohibit the mechanical re-energisation of the remedy by simple agitation, in that they absorb the larger part of any mechanical energy so applied; and thus are not suitable for long-term storage.

At first sight, the construction of a mathematical model would seem a daunting task, but, as we shall see, it is by no means unattainable; and we shall take it in easy and logical stages. In this respect, you must bear in mind that the numerical values selected are fundamentally for the purpose of illustration of principle, and are not to be considered as absolute; and that this in itself does not detract from their ability to express the relationship between different methods of potentisation.

In contrast with molecular 'promotion', which is progressively achieved at any dilution according to the number of succussions, and is only limited by the attainment of saturation, potency or frequency is more limited in its development. Once the diluent molecules have achieved maximum amplitude for a particular frequency, no amount of further succussion will elevate them to a faster oscillation. This is why, in this respect, serial dilution is necessary; for such dilution diminishes that amplitude, whilst maintaining the previous frequency, and enables a new burst of succussion to raise that frequency to a higher level.

We shall consider, therefore, that each serial dilution of any scale can only 'support' a limited number of succussions, as far as potency or frequency is concerned. The relationship between the dilution factor D (the reciprocal of the dilution) and the maximum number of 'allowable' succussions S may be considered as a power regression of formula

$$y = Ax^B,$$

where y=S, x=D, and both A and B are constants.

Assuming that S for a centesimal dilution (where D=100) is 10, and S for an LM dilution (where D=50000) is 100, we may now establish mathematically the values of A and B. A turns out to be 1.815, and B, 0.3705:

$$S = 1.815(D^{0.3705})$$

Just to check our equation, let us solve it for the centesimal and LM scales respectively:

[c] $S = 1.815(100^{0.3705}) = 9.997$
[LM] $S = 1.815(50000^{0.3705}) = 99.964$

As you see, these values of S are close enough to those we wish to express. S, of course, must always be an integer, since practically we cannot allow for fractions of one succussion.

We can now calculate the value of S for the decimal scale:

$$S = 1815(10^{0.3705}) = 4.260,$$

which, to the nearest integer is 4. So, as far as frequency is concerned, the application of 10 succussions per stage of serial dilution will achieve no more than 4.

The generation of frequency is a complex matter. As previously postulated, whereas the creation of the dynamic field is a function of the spontaneous metastable loss of orbitonic quanta, the field also receives energy from other sources. The more important of these is the conversion of the translational kinetic energy of molecular or ionic motion induced by succussion into an electromagnetic form. The other is the contribution made by inadsorbable orbitons (see Element XXII). If the development of frequency were solely dependent upon the rate of spontaneous loss of orbitonic quanta, which must reach a maximum when the diluent is fully saturated, then it would not be possible to increase the frequency by further succussion thereafter (the *maintenance* of frequency in the resting diluent, however, is determined by the metastable loss of orbitons). It follows, therefore, that the mathematical values of frequency cannot be determined in relation to the theoretical level of promotional saturation.

Further complications also arise with regard to the lower liquid dilutions. The presence of molecules and ions of solute (especially the smaller ones) interferes with the development of coherent diluent frequency; since they develop oscillatory frequencies in their own right which conflict with those typical of the diluent (sugars and starches are probably of too great a molecular size to act in this way). This, by the way, is yet another reason why high potencies of Sodium chloride cannot develop in sea-water (see Element XXIII). This effect will vary according to the relative molecular (or ionic) masses of the solute components and their molar concentration; and thus will differ considerably between numerically equivalent dilutions of dissimilar substances, or apparently similar mother tinctures of plant materials, which may vary in concentration. Since, however, frequency cannot be developed without energisation of diluent molecules, it follows that a reasonable molecular or ionic presence is required to produce the requisite collisions.

As a base for calculation, therefore, we must consider those levels of numerical potency where such factors are virtually absent, and where the initial concentration of the solute and the relative masses of its constituent particles are immaterial. To this end, we shall select LM1, 4c prepared from a lactose trituration, and 7x, prepared similarly. With regard to each scale, the presence of the intended solute is minimal and the number of 'promoted' moieties virtually the same for each remedy (see Element XXV).

Before we proceed in this direction, the idea of the *notional frequency* must be introduced. All our calculations are based upon this concept. The notional frequency f_n (expressed in 'åHz') is considered to be a mathematical function of the *real* frequency f (expressed in Hz), where as one increases so does the other. For the moment, this definition will suffice.

The notional frequencies generated at LMl, 4c and 7x following dissolution of the appropriate lactose triturations (3c, 3c and 6x respectively), being the first produced in each such scale, shall be defined as *basal frequencies* f_{bn} (lactose, as has been suggested, cannot develop oscillatory frequencies).

Having defined the relationship between the maximum number of 'allowable' successions S and the dilution factor D, it is now pertinent to express the relationship of β with f_n, where β is the actual number of 'allowable' successions applied, which must be less than or equal to S; that is to say, S is the maximum value of β (the development of frequency is very much dependent upon the number of 'allowable' successions applied at each stage of serial dilution). This may be expressed as

$$f_{bn} = h(\log_{10}\beta),$$

where h is a constant. Selecting h as 0.2, we arrive at

$$f_{bn} = 0.2(\log_{10}\beta) \ \{åHz\}$$

Solving this equation for LM1 [β=100], 4c [β=10], 4c [β=2] and 7x [β=4]:

$$[LM1, \beta=100] \ f_{bn} = 0.2(\log_{10}100) = 0.2(2) = 0.40åHz$$
$$[4c, \beta=10] \ f_{bn} = 0.2(\log_{10}10) = 0.2(1) = 0.20åHz$$
$$[4c, \beta=2] \ f_{bn} = 0.2(\log_{10}2) = 0.2(0.30) = 0.06åHz$$
$$[7x, \beta=4] \ f_{bn} = 0.2(\log_{10}4) = 0.2(0.60) = 0.12åHz$$

You should note the result where β=1:

$$f_{bn} = 0.2(\log_{10}1) = 0.2(0.00) = 0.00åHz$$

This is a mathematical way of stating that 1 succussion achieves no development of frequency at all. This, in fact, is probably fairly close to the truth. When the pharmacist gives the odd succussion intermittently to revive his stored liquid potencies, he more likely raises the amplitude of molecular oscillation rather than the frequency.

As the scales are ascended, f_n develops from f_{bn} as a function of N, the numerical potency. This may be expressed as a logarithmic regression formula of the type

$$y = (Q.lnx) + (R),$$

where $y=f_n$; $x=N$; $lnx=\log_e x$ (where e is the base for natural logarithms, with an approximate value of 2.718); and Q and R are constants which vary with the value of f_{bn} (and hence β). R may be positive or negative.

In order to deduce the values of Q and R in each case (which solution must be carried out individually for each value of f_{bn}), we require a minimum of two known points f_n*N which define the relationship of f_n with N. The lower one for each case is already known:

[LM,β=100] 0.40*1
[c,β=10] 0.20*4
[c,β=2] 0.06*4
[x,β=4] 0.12*7

There remains, therefore, to define an upper point for each case. Since, by virtue of their physical properties, there is an upper limit of frequency expression by diluent molecules, it is not unreasonable to consider that, at a value of N=100000 on any scale, f_n always has the same value. The problem is that we cannot define the point simply as $f_n?*100000$.

We must be able to define the value of $(f_n?)$. One simple approach, which might suffice, is to merely give it an arbitrary value. This in itself is not as unsatisfactory mathematically as it might at first seem, since the general spatial relationship of the graphs of f_n against N would be preserved whichever value might be selected; and it is, indeed, their relationship with which we are mainly concerned. We shall assume, for the sake of argument, that the value of f_n corresponding to N=100000 on any scale is approximately 3.74âHz. Later, you will see that this value is not quite as arbitrary as it may appear; but, for the moment, we shall leave its significance in abeyance.

We have now defined our upper point as 3.74*100000 for all scales, and, therefore, are now able to find the values for Q and R in each case, based upon the logarithmic regression formula defined previously. Placing them appropriately in this formula for each case, we arrive at the following:

[LM,β=100] f_n = (0.290InN) + 0.400
[c,β=10] f_n = (0.349InN) − 0.280
[c,β=2] f_n = (0.363InN) − 0.443
[x,β=4] f_n = (0.379InN) − 0.619

This enables us to calculate any value of f_n for any value of N equal to or greater than the base numerical potency, viz. 1 for the LM scale, 4 for either centesimal, and 7 for the decimal. The mathematical structure conceptualises the fact that the graphic difference between the scales is more apparent in the lower dilutions than the higher; all converging towards the point 3.74*10000 (f_n*N).

Figure 26.1 clearly illustrates the situation up to N=30, where N is plotted

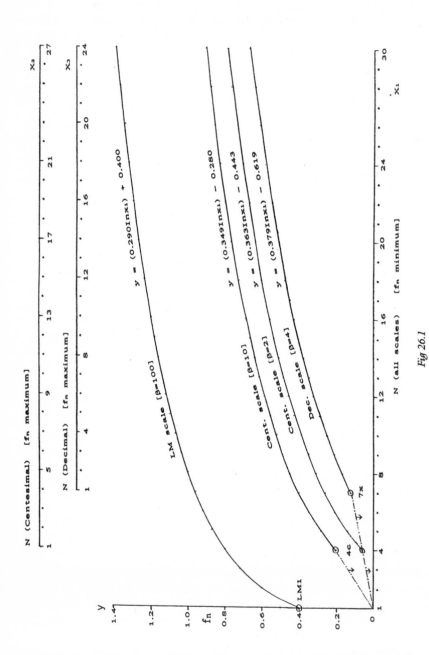

Fig 26.1

on the x-axis, and f_n on the y-axis. Curiously, you will observe that two alternative x-axes are given at the head of the figure, one for the centesimal scale and one for the decimal. This must be explained.

So far, we have only considered the notional frequencies developed by solutions prepared from triturated lactose potencies. Obviously, in actual practice, many remedies are prepared in the liquid phase from the outset, provided that they are soluble in ethanol-water of various strengths. Under ideal conditions of high relative molecular mass and concentration, it is theoretically possible for a 1c to achieve the notional basal frequency value of our lactose-based 4c, and for a 1x to achieve that of our lactose-based 7x. The alternative x-axes express this possibility, setting N=1 against N=4 for centesimals, and N=1 against N=7 for decimals. This then allows us, for any liquid numerical potency, prepared in any manner, which is greater than or equal to the basal potency (4c, 7x), to calculate the notional frequency as a range, defined by an upper and lower limit. The lower limit is always determined by using the basic x-axis x_1, and the upper limit by using the alternative x-axis; x_2 for a centesimal preparation, and x_3 for a decimal. For example, the range for any liquid preparation of 9c [β=10] is 0.49–0.59åHz.

The problem comes when we wish to consider numerical potencies which are lower than the basal potencies 4c and 7x. Of course, lactose triturations have no frequency; or, if you like, one of 0.00åHz. However, liquid preparations can exhibit frequencies; although, as we have said, this is a murky area for quantification. The straight broken lines that are drawn on figure 26.1 define the upper limits of frequency with respect to the x_1-axis. Consulting the graph, you will see that the notional frequency, where N=1, is 0.00åHz on either of the centesimal scales or the decimal. For 6x [β=4] the upper limit of frequency is 0.10åHz, as defined by the broken line, and the lower is 0.00åHz as defined by the x_1-axis itself. In terms of this axis, the range of possible frequencies for 6x [β=4] is, therefore, 0.00–0.10åHz. For simplicity, this is better expressed as a mean #, viz. #0.05.

The true upper limit of f_n for 6x [β=4] is then determined by utilising the x_3-axis, whereby the value is found to be 0.32åHz. The true range for 6x [β=4] notional frequencies is thus expressed as #0.05–0.32åHz. In comparison, the range for 6c [β=10] is 0.35–0.49åHz, and the frequency value for LM6 [β=100], which is fixed, is 0.92åHz. This gives us some numerical comparison of frequency development of identical numerical potencies of different scales. Notice how the LM scale is much better at developing such frequency than its rivals.

As the scales are ascended, so the gradient of each graph diminishes; as a result of which, the range of notional frequency (as determined from the major and alternative x-axes) for any particular potency diminishes in breadth. For example, the range for 16c [β=10] is 0.69–0.75åHz, and for 16x [β=4] it is 0.43–0.55åHz. At 1000x [β=4], the range is 1.999–2.001!

We must now examine the relationship between notional (f_n) and real (f) frequencies. The virtue of notional frequencies lies in their comparative value with regard to the theoretical development of frequency of one scale versus another. However, it would be rather satisfying to translate them into real terms, if at all feasible. This can only be done by taking experimental results[28], so few as there are, into consideration. We should be aware, therefore, that the range of real frequencies for remedies might cover the bulk of the audio frequencies (up to 20000Hz); also that a 1000x potency might have a frequency of around 9725Hz, and a 6x prepared *ab initio* in the liquid phase, one of around 300Hz. Indeed, the mystical notional upper frequency value of 3.74åHz at N=100000, irrespective of scale, was calculated upon this basis. Furthermore, as it turns out, f is more or less directly proportional to f_n:

$$f = g.f_n,$$

where g is a constant with a value of approximately 4865.

As previously determined, the value of the notional frequency for 1000x [β=4] is essentially 2.00åHz (range 1.999–2.001åHz). Therefore,

$$f = 4865 \times 2.00 = 9730Hz$$

This is close to the experimental value of 9725Hz.

The value for 6x [β=4] is in the range #0.05–0.32åHz. Multiplying the limits of the notional range by 4865, we obtain a real range of 243–1557Hz. This range contains the experimental value of 300Hz.

In order to determine the upper limit of real frequency, we must multiply the notional frequency of 3.74åHz by 4865, which produces a real frequency of 18195Hz, where N=100000; which is quite close to the maximum level for audio frequencies.

Our mathematical model of frequency, and thus potency, bears some valuable relationship to experimental reality. It should be emphasised, however, that whilst the graphs suggest a continuous variation of frequency against numerical potency, the frequencies that are interposed between the numerical potency integers are 'disallowable'. That is to say, coherent frequency is discontinuous or quantised. The coherent frequency must jump from one level to the next without any intermediate coherent state being possible. This, of course, does not rule out the possibility of an intermediate incoherent state for the diluent molecules themselves.

Thy cattle-trough floweth over

The matter of *amplitude* must now be discussed. Generally, we may assume that a liquid potency, by virtue of succussion, automatically develops the maximum amplitude permissible for a particular frequency. As the frequency rises, so must the maximum permissible amplitude diminish, in accordance with the physical properties of the diluent molecules; and this relationship is probably one of an exponential regression:

$$y = K.e^{Jx},$$

where y is the amplitude ∂; x is the real frequency f; e is the base for natural logarithms; and K and J are constants.

Assuming, for the sake of argument, a maximum permissible amplitude of 100 notional units at 1Hz and a minimum amplitude of 1 at 18195Hz, then

$$\partial = 100.025(e^{-0.000253f})$$

Upon this basis, $\partial = 50.00$ when f=2739Hz (f_n=0.56åHz), which corresponds to 11c [β=10]. For LM30 [β=100], where the notional frequency is 1.39åHz, and thus the real frequency is $1.39 \times 4865 = 6762$Hz, ∂=18.08.

The next point to consider is the effect of simple dilution, without succussion, upon amplitude. As commented upon previously, there must always be some degree of agitation upon unsuccussed simple dilution; and this, in itself, produces a measure of energisation of both dynamic field and diluent molecules. However, it is possible to itemise certain constructive statements with regard to this matter:

(1) All presuccussive serial dilutions are simple in type, until succussion is applied. The reduction in amplitude consequent upon simple

dilution must be such that the resultant amplitude is equal to, or less than, the maximum permissible amplitude of the consecutive higher and 'allowable' frequency.

(2) LM potencies are generally given in simple dilution by mixing them with water. Hahnemann did not recommend exceeding a simple dilution of $1:3.125 \times 10^5$. Whether he had experimented with further simple dilutions or not, only to find those preparations ineffective, is, of course, purely speculative. However, the possibility remains that, at further simple dilutions, amplitude (and thus frequency), at least for LM30 [$\beta=100$], is extinguished.

(3) A personal communication, from one versed in such matters, informs me that 40 drops (about 2.5ml) of a 30% ethanol preparation dispersed in approximately 227500 litres of water appeared not to achieve the predicted result for veterinary purposes. This was, in fact, a simple dilution of $1:9.1 \times 10^7$.

(4) In contrast, 4ml of liquid potency in a cattle-trough containing about 455 litres of water, appears to be routinely effective. This represents a simple dilution of $1:1.138 \times 10^5$.

With regard to simple unsuccussed dilution, therefore, it would seem imprudent to exceed that level suggested by Hahnemann, viz. $1:3.125 \times 10^5$. Whereas I have ascribed the phenomenon of simple dilutional extinction largely to the consequent and significant reduction of molecular amplitude, the considerable reduction in concentration of imprinted diluent molecules must also count for something. Further experiments must be carried out, in order to determine the true critical level of extinction for remedies prepared according to different scales of potentisation.

It should be remembered that amplitude is probably quantised or discontinuous, as is frequency. It follows that there must be a minimal permissible amplitude, after which, upon further dilution, both frequency and amplitude absent themselves.

It remains to make some further observations on the kinetic energy of diluent oscillation. I have tended to assume that both ethanol and water have the same potential for oscillatory frequency, which is probably the case. But is it true to also assume that their capacity for amplitude is at least similar? After all, ethanol has a much greater relative molecular mass than water. Rather like Oliver Hardy, it might move in more delicate ways. However, it is a plain and clinical fact that ethanol-water is a better homoeopathic medium than water alone, and not merely because of its microbiological preservative function. If it were capable of similar degrees of oscillatory amplitude, then it would, by virtue of its relative molecular mass, carry more kinetic energy, and thus be more resistant to simple dilutional extinction. However, against this must be levelled the fact that, for a given volume of either liquid, the molar concentration of ethanol is considerably less than that of pure water. Nevertheless, the possibility remains that ethanol holds and retains, by virtue of a more ideal conformation, kinetic energy better than pure water.

Chacun à son goût

Having deduced the probable physical nature of remedies, and having understood the principal theoretical differences between the major scales of serial potentisation, we are now ready to consider the action of homoeopathic preparations in the biological situation.

In fact, homoeopathic bioactivity is of two types. The first is the *direct action* upon the cells and tissues of the organism, following systemic absorption. The second, and no less important, is the *indirect action* via the nervous system, to which Hahnemann makes fleeting reference in the Organon[16]. Unfortunately, since the former is readily investigable by means of *in vitro* experimentation, and the latter is not, seldom is reference made to this indirect mechanism, or its significance fully appreciated. The ultimate effect of any remedy *in vivo is* not only dependent upon both its physical nature and direct action, but also upon whether the indirect mechanism also applies; and this, in turn, is dependent upon the method of administration.

The standard method of dosage is via the oral route. In this way, both liquid and solid preparations usually come into intimate contact with the lining of the mouth and oropharynx. This area of the anatomy contains the prime receptor sites for the indirect route of biological action via the nervous system. Though certainly not in all cases, the patient may experience what is described as an 'unpleasant taste', quite uncharacteristic of that of the normal diluent itself; and this has been held to indicate that the remedy is well-suited to the patient in one respect or another (this perversion of taste may be akin to that experienced by patients taking conventional lithium medication for psychiatric disorder). This observation was first brought to my attention many years ago by the distinguished homoeopathic pharmacist, John Ainsworth; and which has been corroborated on many occasions in my own clinical practice, and, indeed, with regard to myself. Hence, it is not unreasonable to surmise that the homoeopathic nervous receptors are within the abundant *taste-buds* themselves, which are, by their very nature, admirably suited to the detection of minute quantities of substance. These modified taste receptors recognise, and respond to, both imprinted molecules and certain chemicals of distinctive taste; the transmission of taste being their minor function. This provides an explanation for the general belief that *peppermint* (which contains menthol, $C_{10}H_{20}O$) or other strong-tasting substances[2] (such as onion, which contains allyl propyl disulphide, $C_6H_{12}S_2$) may interfere with the action of the remedy; for, once having been so powerfully stimulated, the modified taste receptor will be numbed for a *short* time to any further stimulation by any substance. Since this period of sensory inertia is usually no more than ten minutes or so, it is unnecessary to ban mint-flavoured toothpastes during homoeopathic therapy, provided that the remedy is administered at some respectable interval from tooth-brushing. On the other hand, the contamination of pilules or tablets with perfumed or other pungent substances (especially camphor, $C_{10}H_{16}O$), by incorrect handling, may result in simultaneous competition at the taste-bud level; and thus is to be considered as undesirable. Sweet-tasting substances, such as lactose and ethanol, do not appear to interfere with the mechanism; nor do hot-tasting substances, such as chili and ginger, appear to exert any deleterious effect in this regard.

We are justified in proposing an indirect or nervous route, in that remedies, in certain situations, may act with great speed. The remedy Arnica montana, administered orally in potency, will take the pain from a crushed finger in seconds. There are those, of course, who will argue that rapid absorption occurs through the lining of the mouth, and, in this way they account for the speed of action. However, experiences with the conventional drug nitroglycerine, which is administered sublingually in the treatment of angina, suggest that it takes approximately three minutes to act[14]. With potentised Arnica, we are talking in terms of seconds, not minutes! The plain fact of the matter is that transmucosal absorption is too sluggish a route to account for this rapidity.

There is usually a certain relationship between the biological action of a remedy and that which is normally associated with its crude drug of origin. This action is generally *opposite*, but may, in some cases, be *similar*. Similarity of action is exemplified by *aggravation*, *healing crisis* and *proving*. There are also those remedies which consistently mimic the normal action of the crude drug. Arnica, for example, whether administered orally in potency (6c–1M) or applied locally as a mother tincture, will act with almost equal efficacy on simple bruises. Euphrasia, in its action upon the eye, behaves similarly. Oestradiol 12c frequently alleviates menopausal hot flushes, as does crude oestrogen in general.

However, when the patient holds a minute quantity of crude unpotentised

Arnica, Euphrasia or Oestradiol in her mouth, no effect, apart from the sensation of taste, is experienced; the bruise, the conjunctivitis, or the hot flushes remain unalleviated. Yet, we have deduced that a remedy is a chemical imprint of sorts of the crude drug of origin, and we know that it will act when held in the mouth, just as that drug does when administered systemically or topically (locally). How does the modified taste receptor reject the crude drug and accept its homoeopathic representative? Similarly, we may enquire, where the action of the systemic drug and the potentised remedy are opposite, why small doses of the crude drug held in the mouth produce neither an opposite action nor, indeed, any action at all?

In effect, we have demanded to know the difference between a post-box and an elephant. The modified taste receptors certainly know the difference; for, even if the remedy has some 'peculiar taste' (and bearing in mind that even tiny amounts of chemicals are detectable by tasting), it never invokes that of the crude drug itself.

These receptors are sensitive to non-ionic molecules with the property of *coherent oscillation*; in other words, those of imprinted water and ethanol. Their coherent oscillatory function is their principal signature for recognition, and such *established* coherency is only marginally impaired by the presence of dissolved ions within the saliva (see Element XXVI for the effect of small molecules and ions on the *generation* of frequency). Once stimulated, the receptors send encoded information to the central nervous system, concerning the nature of the chemical imprint, and the frequency of molecular oscillation and its amplitude. The central nervous system evaluates the pathophysiological status of the body, and determines whether the incoming information is intelligible in terms of corrective adjustment. Should that information be inappropriate, it is then generally rejected, and no physiological changes ensue. Appropriate information, however, is duly processed, and a biological response follows. The perfect response would be one of improvement without aggravation, but this will only occur if the nature of the incoming homoeopathic message is correctly matched against the sensitivity of the processing function of the central nervous system. The degree of receptor stimulation is important in this respect, and this is related to the concentration of imprinted diluent molecules at the receptor site of the taste-buds. This, in turn, is determined by the method and level of potentisation, the degree of any simple dilution subsequently applied, and the material dose given. Excessive stimulation, by too great a concentration of imprinted molecules at the receptor site, will sometimes result in physiological aggravation. The repetition of dose too frequently may also result in the same. However, the sensitivity of the central processing function must also be taken into consideration in the matter of homoeopathic aggravation, and in many individuals it is not so delicate as to engender this phenomenon readily. In others, it is so delicately balanced that aggravation seems to occur with the slightest indiscretion in dosage. Indeed, it is these sensitive subjects upon whom remedies may be readily experimentally *proven*; for, irrespective of their need for physiological correction, the central mechanism, almost routinely, processes the encoded information from the mouth and produces an effect initially similar to that of the crude drug. The antidotal effect of *coffee* (which contains aromatic substances, such as 2-furylmethanethiol, C_5H_6OS) is ascribable to its interference with central processing (since tea also contains caffeine, and has no such antidotal effect, this substance does not account for this action).

As we have discussed in Element XX, the *range* of action of the correctly selected remedy is, in general, determined by its oscillatory frequency, and hence its numerical potency. Frequency also, along with nervous receptor molecular concentration, contributes to the determination of strength of action (the term *strength of action* incorporates the concepts of speed, efficacy and duration). However, the *amplitude* of diluent oscillation, as with molecular concentration at the receptor site, is related to the potential for aggravation (both of which are reduced by simple dilution). Indeed, it may well be that it is even more important in this respect than the matter of concentration. The greater the amplitude, the more likely the production of aggravation. The amplitude, as we have seen, is inversely related to the frequency, so that lower frequencies (and thus numerical potencies) have higher amplitudes. This may account for the belief that lower potencies are more likely to induce aggravation. This effect, of course, is countered by the lesser concentration of imprinted molecules at the receptor site, and, through this alone, is not so common occurrence as one might be led to believe. The use of simple dilution of the potentised remedy prior to administration reduces amplitude in all cases; but it must be emphasised that those preparations of initially lower amplitude (viz. the higher numerical potencies) will stand less dilution before they are extinguished in terms of frequency.

Fortunately, in the majority of cases, the central processing system is tolerant of a wide range of that information which qualifies the chemical imprint. In many individuals, the ranges of amplitude and receptor molecular concentration (and numbers of receptors so stimulated) which are tolerated without over- or under-stimulation are considerable. These are, in practice, more relevant to sensitive subjects. Hence, in this respect, the initial material dose, be it one drop (or pilule) or three, and the degree of any pre-administrative simple dilution, are often virtually immaterial in the majority of cases.

At the receptor site of the taste-bud, energy passes from the imprinted diluent molecule to the receptor cell. In this way, that molecule sheds its amplitude and thus its frequency, which become zero. At the same time, the promoted electrons of the hydroxyl group are depromoted to their normal orbital status, and the imprint thus removed.

I have been careful, thus far, to avoid discussing the so-called *tissue salts* and any other pure lactose triturations. It has been suggested previously that these lack the facility for coherent oscillation in their solid state. However, upon dissolution in the saliva, and energised by the muscular movements of the oral structures, the molecules of salivary water indulge, to a degree, in effective collision with those of lactose, so becoming imprinted similarly. Nevertheless, since the dissolved ions of the saliva interfere with the development of coherent oscillation, those imprinted molecules of lactose and water are denied functional access to the oral receptor sites. Tissue salts and the like are, therefore, probably committed solely to the exhibition of direct action, to which we must shortly pass.

It should also be observed that *solvation* effects influence the ability of dissolved lactose to pass its imprint to salivary water. Water molecules become attached by means of hydrogen bonds to the lactose hydroxyl groups, which thus interfere with free collision. Such bonds can be ruptured by mechanical action, but this is seldom of great force in the mouth. Since many of these bonds, therefore, remain intact, many lactose hydroxyl groups fail to induce an imprint upon water. This explains the necessity for giving larger material doses of lactose triturations (say, four pellets or tablets for an adult) than those required for liquid potencies presented in pilular form (where one pilule is often sufficient, even for an adult).

The direct action of orally-administered remedies must be preceded by their systemic absorption. Injection of liquid potencies (as favoured in Continental Europe) and topical application (as with Graphites 8x cream) lead to direct action alone, by bypassing the indirect route. The administration of liquid potencies by inhalation of their vapours may produce both indirect and direct effects; the former by the stimulation of the receptors of the oropharynx by the oscillating vaporous diluent, and the latter via absorption through the nasal and pharyngeal mucous membranes.

*T*ransportation as a means of correction

Before proceeding with an analysis of the *direct action* of remedies, we must discuss certain important aspects of those which have been given orally, this being by far the most popular method of administration:

(1) How they are affected by dilution with saliva.
(2) How they are affected by dilution with gastric contents.
(3) How and where they are systemically absorbed.
(4) How they are transported to their target site.
(5) How they replicate.

In Element XXVIII, for the sake of simplicity, the effect of saliva upon the remedy was not mentioned, except with regard to lactose triturations. As with the latter, a certain degree of imprinting of salivary water molecules probably occurs with remedies in general. However, it is likely that a proportion of imprinted molecules of both water and ethanol are rapidly bound to salivary protein, which term includes the glycoprotein *mucin* and the enzyme *ptyalin* (salivary amylase); this occurring as a result of electrostatic attraction and hydrogen bonding (a small proportion of imprinted ethanol and water molecules also become incorporated in ionic hydration shells). This effectively protects the small groups of imprinted molecules from further dilution by the aqueous component of saliva. Nevertheless, upon contact with the oropharyngeal mucosal surface, these groups of bound molecules may be released from their binding protein (perhaps by some active or electrostatically preferable process), and, together with those already free, are absorbed by the mucosa itself. The remainder of those so bound pass to the stomach.

The human stomach, the maximum volume of which, in the adult, is about 1–1.5 litres, actually varies greatly in its capacity between individuals, and its contents at any particular time, according to intake of fluid and food.

Considering the result of one pilule, which contains approximately 0.0006ml of liquid potency, being dissolved in, say, 1 litre of stomach contents, this would give a v/v dilution of about $1:1.6\times10^6$. The binding of the imprinted molecules to salivary protein resists this immense dilution, and also prevents their adsorption to the organic food content, with consequent inactivation. Their release at the gastric mucosal surface results in absorption.

The absorption of remedies may occur via any mucosal surface to which they have access, including that of the nasal cavity and the conjunctiva. The small groups of imprinted ethanol or water molecules are transported (perhaps actively) to the tiny circulatory capillaries of the mucosa, their integrity and oscillation being preserved by the electromagnetic dynamic field which exists between them. Here they become bound to the blood proteins, adsorbed to the surfaces of white and red blood cells and platelets, and become incorporated in hydration shells around ionic substances, such as Na^+Cl^-. In this manner, they are transported throughout the body and to their target sites.

However, their initial number is insufficiently large to produce much effect, and there must, therefore, be some way in which they replicate. Their prior replication within the saliva is hampered by protein binding and relatively poor mechanical energisation, and thus is of little consequence.

Replication occurs in the circulatory system in a special way; which, in itself, is a particular form of potentisation that increases the number of imprinted molecules, whilst preserving (and not increasing) their frequency (and thus potency). This occurs dominantly within the lumina of the heart and large arteries, where the cellular, molecular and ionic particles of the blood are caused to collide with great force. Here, the imprinted molecules bound to the surfaces of protein and blood cells, and those incorporated in ionic hydration shells transfer their imprint to normal water molecules disposed similarly. Their binding to blood proteins, cells or ions protects them from the super-dilution which would occur if they were free within the substance of the blood. Since the generation of frequency is impaired by lack of molecular freedom, and is thus hampered where the imprinted molecules are bound to other particles, frequency of oscillation is communicated in a particular way. There is probably an exchange of water or ethanol molecules upon collision between the various binding particles, so that those which are coherently oscillating arrive in groups of bound water molecules not yet exhibiting this phenomenon. In such a way, the level of frequency, as determined by that of the original oral dose, is transmitted to those recipient groups (a similar process of transfer of imprint and frequency could conceivably occur in the early stages of normal potentisation; that is to say, in the lower dilutions, where the original substance still remains). Any free water molecules within the blood gaining homoeopathic energisation are diluted to such a degree by the blood volume itself, that they cannot form a dynamic field. Their energised existence is transient and inconsequential.

Since the groups of bound oscillating molecules are so small, the energy of the field-molecular system of each is low and unstable. As repeated forceful collisions occur, this energetic status rises, but becomes insupportable by that system. At some critical point, this energy is rapidly released, with the disappearance of the dynamic field, the 'depromotion' of imprinted molecules, and their loss of oscillatory frequency. The functional life expectancy of the imprinted molecular groups in the blood is probably in the order of minutes.

The blood, therefore, does not produce a cohesive dynamic field involving the imprinted molecules, but rather is composed of numerous bound groups of such molecules, each with its own field. These are readily transferred, according to the nature of the pathology, by means of proteins, red or white blood cells, platelets or ions, from the blood to the target site. This transfer may occur in seconds or minutes; a period of time well within the brief life-expectancy within the cardiovascular system of the bound imprinted groups. Upon removal from the collisional violence of the circulation, their existence is preserved for a greater period, but replication is no longer mechanically feasible.

Deceptor theory

Due to the method of replication of the remedy within the cardiovascular system, the dominant imprinted molecule becomes water, even though ethanol may have been the major component of the original dose. Therefore, in considering the direct effect of remedies, we are, almost exclusively, concerned with the properties of potentised water itself. The efficiency of the replication system is such, that almost irrespective of initial material dosage (beyond some tiny minimum), the blood achieves high levels of imprinted molecular groups in a very short time. Hence, whether the initial dose is one pilule or ten, the result is similar.

Even without proposing the existence of any active mechanism, the imprinted water molecules are readily released from their binding or carrier particles (be they ionic, cellular or proteic) by the natural competition of normal water molecules of the tissue fluids for occupancy of binding sites. Hence, those remedial molecules may then gain access to their sites of action upon the tissues.

The usual way in which a crude drug acts is via its attachment to a macromolecular component of a cell, termed a *receptor* (although, perhaps more correctly, it should be termed a *pharmacological receptor*, in order to prevent confusion with a *nervous receptor*, such as the taste-bud). The receptors, which are usually proteins, may be situated upon the cellular membrane or within the substance of the cell; and, for each drug, there are probably several thousand specific receptor sites per cell. Some drugs, of course, do not act via receptors. Sodium bicarbonate, for example, in its neutralisation of stomach acidity, acts by a direct chemical reaction between itself and hydrochloric acid.

The direct action of a remedy is often ascribable to its occupation of those specific receptors which would normally attract the attention of the crude drug of origin. Let us, therefore, initially turn our attention to the relationship between drugs and receptors.

The attraction of a crude drug molecule to its receptor is sometimes conceptualised as a correspondence of geometry. The male molecule fits the shape of the female receptor. While shape and size as such may have some limited role, in that the molecule must be able to physically approximate itself to the receptor site, there are other facets of drug-receptor attraction which are of greater importance. Both the drug and its receptor must be attracted electrochemically. That is to say, the outermost electronic orbitals of the receptor must be attractive to those of the drug molecule, in order for them to have any functional and specific relationship. Attraction is followed by *binding*. The binding of drugs to receptors involves all known types of interaction[14], viz. hydrogen, ionic, van der Waals' and covalent; and, in many situations, multiple interactions are manifest.

The action of the crude drug at the receptor site is sometimes one of *antagonism*, where the *inert* drug (the *antagonist*) blocks the receptor site and denies a competitive *active* substance (the *agonist*) access to it. This occurs, for example, where the attachment of acetylcholine to the muscle receptors is blocked by curare, thus leading to paralysis. In such cases, there is no stimulation of the receptor, but merely a denial of stimulation by blockade.

The alternative type of action is where the active crude drug (the *agonist*) actually stimulates the receptor to produce some biochemically-based physiological *response*. This response may be *zero, characteristic* or *inverse*, according to the number of specific receptors stimulated upon or within the cell.

A *zero* response to an agonistic drug is a consequence of subliminal dosage, inadequate absorption or inadequate transport, where only a small fraction of the cell's specific receptor sites become occupied by drug molecules.

A *characteristic* response occurs where a large proportion (though not necessarily all) of those receptors are activated by the drug; which is the usual state of affairs with the administration of significant material doses.

An *inverse* response occurs as a result of a receptor occupancy between the upper limit for the zero response and the lower limit for the characteristic response. This intermediate state is usually associated with the administration of the drug at a dosage below that used to produce a characteristic response, but may also be due to impairment of the absorptive or transportive processes. An inverse response, as the title suggests, is the opposite of the characteristic response. One characteristic property of crude belladonna is the production of delirium; so, the opposite, or inverse, effect is the removal of delirium. Indeed, Hahnemann himself utilised the inverse response in his early development of homoeopathy, where he gave small *unpotentised* doses of drugs to heal the sick. This variability of response, according to the proportion of cellular receptor occupancy, may be regarded as a develop-

ment of what is termed the *Arndt-Schulz Law* (or *Hueppe's Rule*) of the late
nineteenth century; the original of which states that 'for every drug, small
doses stimulate, moderate doses inhibit, and large doses kill'; our
modification of which states that 'for many drugs, small doses have the
opposite or inverse effect of larger sublethal doses.' It is quite clear that the
specific receptor group of the cell may produce alternative biochemical
pathways, according to their collective level of stimulation. This, in itself,
accounts for many apparently anomalous or idiosyncratic responses to
orthodox medication, where, although the drug has been given in significant
dosage, it has failed to reach the cellular receptors in sufficient quantity; or,
alternatively, that the cell is so diseased that a good proportion of its specific
receptors have been rendered inactive by toxic effect.

Where a crude drug is actually composed of more than one active chemical
or principle, then any response produced is dependent upon its reaction with
a number of functionally dissimilar types of receptor.

Having discussed the action of drugs at the receptor site in some detail,
let us now turn to the action of potentised remedies at the same locus. In
this respect, with regard to the lowest dilutions, the first point, of which we
must dispose, is whether any residual molecules of the original crude drug
can exert any significant effect. Bearing in mind that dilutions below 6x or
3c are seldom employed, and that relatively small material doses of the drug
within its diluent (ethanol-water or lactose) are usually given, to all intents
and purposes, the concentration of the drug at the receptor site is generally
insufficient (except in the case of the most virulent poisons) to produce
anything other than a zero agonistic, or a nil antagonistic, action.

There now remains to be considered the matter of the relationship of the
imprinted water molecule with the receptor. Since the outermost electrons of
this molecule occupy the same energetic orbitals as those of the crude drug
of origin, and its size and shape are generally such to give it access, it is naturally
attracted to the receptor site, as is the case with the drug itself. However, as
we have discussed in Elements XIV and XV, the water molecule is otherwise
chemically dissimilar, and thus is not necessarily bound to the receptor by the
same type of interactions (ionic, etc.) as would be expected with the crude
drug. Because of the efficiency of the blood replication system, there are
generally adequate numbers of imprinted molecules present in the tissues to
occupy all the available specific receptors of the cell.

The action of the imprinted molecule at the receptor site is one of
antagonism or agonism, according to circumstances. When a low potency
(say, 6c) of Arsenicum album is administered to a subject suffering from
arsenic poisoning, the imprinted water molecules compete with the poison

at its receptor sites, and cause it to be displaced (after which, it is excreted). This is an example of antagonism, where the role of imprinted water would appear to be purely passive. In contrast, the same remedy, Arsenicum album 6c, will act agonistically upon the same specific cellular receptors in the treatment of acute gastroenteritis, corresponding to the inverse or opposite action of the crude drug itself. Despite the fact that the drug can only produce this action by intermediate occupancy of receptor sites, the remedy can achieve the same, even though the receptors are apparently saturated (that is to say, fully occupied) by it. Furthermore, the administration of a higher potency (say, Arsenicum album 100c) may produce aggravation of diarrhoea and vomiting in its agonistic effect on the same receptors; thus simulating the characteristic effect of crude arsenic, as associated with its high receptor occupancy. How can the imprinted water molecule demonstrate all three actions (antagonism, inverse agonism and characteristic agonism) by means of occupation of the same receptors?

In fact, in cases of poisoning, the remedy is not purely antagonistic. The antagonism arises simply from the fact that it competes with the poison for binding at the receptor site. At the same time, in general, it exerts an inverse agonistic effect, which opposes the damage to the physiology caused by that poison. Pure antagonism is not the function of an homoeopathic remedy.

Moreover, the direct action of an imprinted water molecule is also dependent upon its oscillatory frequency. The frequency is preserved in the course of the remedy from the site of absorption to the tissues, whereas the amplitude of oscillation is modified by the intervention of the blood potentisation process, and cannot, therefore, be adjusted by pre-administrative dilution. The specific receptors are sensitive to the frequency of oscillation of the imprinted molecules. Speaking generally, their collective effect is to induce inverse response for low frequencies, and an initial characteristic response for high frequencies (imprinted water molecules, originating from tissue salts and other lactose triturations, probably develop low oscillatory frequencies within the cardiovascular system). An initial characteristic response, which is consistent with the notion of aggravation, is normally followed by an inverse phase of improvement, provided that the administration of the higher potency is not repeated in the characteristic phase.

However, these rules are not inflexible. The physiological sensitivity of the subject, the intensity of the pathophysiology, and the nature of the remedy also determine the response. Very sensitive patients may experience the results of characteristic agonism even with low potencies, whilst those more physiologically stolid may tolerate high potencies with no apparent ill-effects. During high febrile states, such as influenza, high potencies may accelerate cure without aggravation; similarly, potentised pollen may be given with impunity in severe cases of hay-fever, as high as 200c. Some remedies, such as Arnica montana, seldom seem to produce anything other than a beneficial effect, irrespective of the potency given.

With regard to direct action, we should now consider what happens when we give a remedy that is not indicated by the particular pathophysiology. This will occur as a result of an incorrect prescription or during the course of an experimental proving of a remedy on a variety of volunteers. The remedy binds to the receptor site, which usually attempts to generate an inverse response. Often, the inverse response is inexpressible. Taking Belladonna as an example: where delirium is not manifest, the removal of delirium is not possible. Thus, even though the receptor has attempted to institute biochemical and physiological changes, the body cannot respond, and nothing is experienced by the subject; which is usually the case. However, in sensitive subjects, even an inappropriate remedy in relatively low potency has the capacity to produce characteristic response; and thus a *proving* occurs, with development of objective and subjective symptomatology, typical of the crude drug of origin.

The production of characteristic response (or aggravation) does imply that homoeopathy has its dangers in the wrong hands, and to say, as is often said, that it is absolutely safe in all circumstances is patent nonsense. Even the finest gun is only as safe as the person who pulls the trigger. Nevertheless, whereas an 'overdose' of remedy may make someone very ill, it is never likely to kill or permanently maim, as the crude drug of origin can, be it a virulent poison, such as arsenic. Thus, what I have termed as the characteristic response of a remedy, is only characteristic of the original crude drug to a degree, and not one of absolute correspondence. This is because the imprinted molecule is not the identical chemical image of the crude drug, but only mimics it in certain limited respects. It is sufficiently similar, in terms of its electronic conformation, to be recognised and bound to the receptor site, yet it is sufficiently dissimilar to fail to impress the receptor that it is anything other than a close relative of the main substance to which it normally responds. Any characteristic response is, therefore, partial and incomplete; as is, no doubt, any inverse response. The dissimilarity is recognisable by the specific receptor in terms of the combination of electrochemical interactions (hydrogen, ionic, etc.) which apply to the binding of a particular species of ion or molecule, and which are unique to that substance.

ELEMENT *XXXI*

*R*ogue water

A source of confusion in homoeopathy is the fact that some practitioners claim that lower potencies produce more aggravation than higher ones, whilst others proclaim the opposite.

Considering firstly the very lowest dilutions of the decimal and centesimal scales (which are seldom administered these days), there may be a sufficient amount of the crude drug remaining to induce an agonistic characteristic response. Rising up the scales, to levels where residual original substance is minimally present, we then have the higher amplitude of the lower frequencies as a possible cause for aggravation, through the indirect action of remedies. In contrast, where the direct action of remedies upon drug receptors is concerned, aggravation is more likely with higher potencies rather than lower. Whether aggravation occurs, or not, thus depends upon the balance of effect of the indirect and direct receptor actions. So-called *pathological* prescribing relies more on the direct action of remedies (except where almost immediate effects are demanded); and so, those who prescribe more pathologically, claim that higher potencies are more inclined to aggravate. Conversely, *constitutional* prescribing leans more heavily on the indirect action for its dissemination of response via the central nervous system; and those who prescribe largely so often claim that lower potencies are more inclined towards the production of aggravation. Those who prescribe betwixt and between, as many quite reasonably do, see aggravations as much with the lower as with the higher potencies (correct use of LM potencies is said to reduce the risk of aggravation, whatever the style of prescribing). Poor centesimal and decimal prescribers, on the other hand, seldom see aggravation at all, the remedies being so ill-matched to the case that only a glancing blow is delivered to the physiology, as though a *feather* had brushed against it.

Another small conundrum to be explained is why some remedies, such as Arnica, Euphrasia and Oestradiol, appear routinely to simulate the characteristic, rather than the inverse, actions of the crude drug?

Aggravation aside, we generally think of the action of homoeopathic potentised remedies as being dominantly inverse. It is a little surprising, therefore, to learn that some are apparently of a different bent. In fact, this difference is illusory. When we apply Arnica mother tincture to the unbroken skin, only a small amount of the substance penetrates into the tissues, and the Arnica cellular receptors are by no means fully occupied. In this way, what is usually thought of as the characteristic action of the drug is none other than the inverse response itself. The phenomenon is further reinforced, in all probability, by traumatic damage to many receptor sites, which thus are rendered incapable of binding and response. A similar argument applies to Euphrasia lotion, which relies for its effect upon intermediate receptor occupancy, favoured by infective or allergic damage to the specific conjunctival receptors. Again, the drug oestradiol probably relies for what appears to be its characteristic effect on such intermediate receptor occupancy; and thus its normal clinical action is, in reality, inverse in nature. In all these cases, therefore, the remedies, as with remedies in general, tend to act in accordance with the inverse rather than the characteristic actions of the drugs.

Let us pass now to the inactivation of remedies in the tissues. All imprinted diluent molecules are subject to metastable decay, and the smaller the group, the more quickly this will happen. In their attachment to specific drug receptors, they donate some of their acquired energy to the receptor macromolecules, and so speed their own debasement to the energetic ground state. However, the question remains as to whether their influence upon the receptor sites ceases when they are 'depromoted'? From experience with high numerical potencies, it might be inferred that their effect upon the drug receptor continues long (perhaps, hours or days) after the time of their theoretical inactivation. That is to say, even after the imprinted molecules have been reduced to the status of normality, and even after their competitive removal from the receptor site, the response which they have induced may continue for some time; so much so, that even the subsequent arrival of a true drug molecule at the same site will not effect any change in receptor response.

We must now consider whether there are any further ways in which remedies might act via the direct route upon tissues; that is to say, ways other than the occupancy of 'classical' drug receptor sites. In this respect, we must now investigate the action of the imprinted water molecule as a form of deviant or rogue water, rather than as an aberrant drug.

Initially, therefore, we must consider one particular role of normal water in the body with regard to various macromolecules, viz. proteins, glycoproteins (carbohydrate + protein), carbohydrates, nucleotides and nucleoproteins (nucleotide + protein). Water appears to exert a significant action in the maintenance and biological function of such biopolymers. As Franks[13] states: 'The transformations of biopolymers from resting to active states, or indeed, their complete inactivation can be brought about by chemically or physically quite minor changes in the solvent medium...' Furthermore: 'It can be concluded that hydration interactions must play a significant part in the maintenance of native macromolecular structures.'

It would seem, therefore, that the introduction of imprinted or rogue water molecules, of deviant molecular orbital conformation and oscillatory activity, could, in this way, result in a change in activity of these biologically essential macromolecules[7]. These include pharmacological receptors themselves, enzymes, and, of course, DNA and RNA. Such an effect could be produced by the interference of imprinted molecular groups with the normal structure of biological water. On the other hand, it could be argued that aberrant hydration interactions are, in reality, no more than the binding of imprinted water molecules to specific homoeopathic receptor sites upon the relevant macromolecules, which are functionally inaccessible to their crude drugs of origin.

The idea should now be introduced that the imprinted water molecule may directly influence the function and response of the drug receptor to which it may be bound, not only via its electrochemical interaction with that site, but also by its possibly more intimate and direct incorporation into the structure and chemistry of the receptor macromolecule itself. This may be, indeed, one of the ways in which the receptor changes towards inverse rather than characteristic response.

The notion that imprinted water may influence genetic material itself is consistent with the profound results of homoeopathy in the treatment of the functional effects of genetic disorders, such as asthma and cystic fibrosis.

The influence of potentised Mercuric chloride on the activity of the extracted enzyme diastase has been soundly demonstrated by means of *in vitro* experiments by Boyd[7]. It was found that, whereas some numerical potencies produced inhibition of the enzymatic hydrolysis of starch (as is demonstrable with the crude substance), others accelerated this process, even if infinitesimal (such as 61x). Since this experiment did not involve any cellular entities, we can only conclude that there was some direct action of the potentised drug upon the enzyme itself, unmediated by any remote cellular receptors. This is consistent with the notion of the remedy interfering with the normal hydration interaction with the enzyme. Furthermore, in terms of our proposed general theory, it would seem that the oscillatory frequency of the remedy, in some way, directly determines the activation or inactivation of enzymatic systems.

It follows, therefore, that the possible actions of a remedy, and sites of action, are manifold. Not only are there indirect actions via the nervous system, there are also multiple direct actions within the tissues; some involving classical receptor macromolecules, and others involving hydration interactions with macromolecules in general. Hence, it is not surprising to find that the remedy is never a pure inverse or characteristic representative of the crude drug of origin, but a derivative that manifests many new and important properties, which are inexpressible by that drug itself. Consultation of the *materia medica homoeopathica* will confirm this fact.

Let us turn now to the matter of microbiological *nosodes* in the prevention and treatment of infective disease[15].

There is, with regard to these remedies, no evidence that they act by directly inducing antibody formation; nor is it particularly likely that they act directly on the infective microorganisms themselves in the manner of antibiotics (although we cannot be sure about that in all cases). Most probably they act dominantly upon the normal receptor sites for infective toxins, exhibiting an antagonistic and inverse agonistic role. Where active disease is present, they no doubt also have an intimate restorative action upon inhibited enzyme systems, in the manner described previously. In so reducing the harmful effects of the infective organism, they assist the immune system in its defensive mechanisms, and in the production of antibodies. The use of intermittent (say, once weekly) doses of a specific nosode in high potency (30c and above) to *prevent* infection is justified in terms of our proposition that the toxic receptor sites may remain insensitive to toxic agonism for some time after the degradation of the remedy within the tissues. However, it is unlikely that prolonged 'immunity', for months or years, can ever be produced by this method (as is the case with orthodox immunisation), and so the nosode must be given repeatedly as long as the person is exposed to the specific infective risk.

The principles governing the prevention and treatment of *allergy*[15] with potentised allergens (e.g. Mixed pollens or Wheat 30c) are similar, in many respects, to those for nosodes. However, in this case, the initial repeated use of these remedies may, in some instances, result in permanent or prolonged desensitisation. Accordingly, further doses are then either unnecessary, or are only required infrequently.

Odds, but not ends

Short of going down a blind alley, which I think we have not, the end of one road is the beginning of another. As my theory has evolved, so numerous quirks of homoeopathy have received sensible explanation. Such a theory would have been impossible without having had the advantage of the admirable theoretical, experimental and clinical observations made by many other authors, to whom much credit is owed. Nevertheless, all that has been produced is no more than a reasonable and provisional clarification of the mechanisms involved, the prime role of which is to make sense out of the mire of information and opinion, and, beyond that, to act as a foundation for further constructive argument. Neither is the mathematics of potentisation intended to be anything other than an illustration of possible reality and an instrument of comparison between different modes of preparation. Those who have seen my ideas in any other light, have failed to grasp my meaning and intention.

Inevitably, there are some loose ends to be tied up, about which sensible questions might be asked, as indeed they should:

(1) *Can the possibility of aggravation with a centesimal potency be reduced by pre-administrative simple dilution?*
Yes. In sensitive subjects, one pilule may be dissolved in a wine glassful of warm water, and half the amount given as a single dose, being held for a few seconds in the mouth. This reduces both the amplitude of oscillation and the concentration of imprinted molecules. Provided that the indirect action is more relevant, then the possibility of aggravation will be reduced. The direct action, however, remains unaffected by such measures.

(2) *What is the theoretical basis for the production of radiation remedies, such as Sol and X-Ray 30c, and the magnetic remedies?*
It is a point of great interest that sunlight may inactivate potentised remedies in general, and yet produce a remedy in its own right. A

vial of plain ethanol-water exposed to any particular type of electromagnetic radiation (sunlight, X-rays, VDU emissions, etc.) for some hours will acquire new properties from them. We might infer that this is yet another example of electronic energy storage by the hydroxyl groups of the diluent. In this case, however, the electrons maintain their normal orbital situation and are not promoted. They do, however, carry specific energy forms (or quanta) that relate to the frequency of the inductive radiation. Such an energised diluent can be subjected to serial potentisation, just as with a normal remedy. Here, orbitonic quanta released from the energised molecules during collision are characteristic of the original radiation, and not of the normal higher orbital energetic status. In the case of magnetic remedies, such as Magnetis polus Australis, the electrons may be forced into new and unconventional orbitals, the energy for this transposition being derived from the thermokinetic energy of the diluent.

(3) *Can remedies pass into the breast-milk, thus making it a useful route for their administration to suckling infants?*
Imprinted diluent molecules may pass into any bodily fluid after replication in the circulatory system, including the milk and the urine. In the milk, they are readily bound to protein.

(4) *What is the theoretical foundation for the antidotal, inimical and complementary relationships of remedies?*
An antidotal remedy merely produces the inverse effects of that which it is opposing. That is to say, its physiological effects are opposite. In terms of the direct action of remedies, the pharmacological receptors involved may be different, with dissimilar responses. Alternatively, both remedies may compete for the same receptor site, at which they produce different responses, or indeed, where one may be the antagonist of the other. Inimical reactions (such as the generation of eczema when Mercurius solubilis and Silicea are given together) are often the result of excessive and rapid detoxification of the diseased tissues by the combined action of the relevant remedies. These either accumulate within the body, so as to affect the function of normal tissues, or are excreted, with irritant action, via the skin. A complementary remedy merely continues the physiological rectification process that the primary remedy is incapable of completing.

(5) *Is mixed prescribing undesirable?*
Provided that remedies are neither antidotal nor inimical, there is no

theoretical, or indeed practical, objection to their use in combination. In fact, there are many standard mixtures in common use, the efficacy of which has been confirmed over many years of clinical experience. Whilst this might be an anathema to the purists, the facts stand as they are.

(6) *Where topical applications, such as creams, are used, is it acceptable to mix potentised remedies with aromatic substances?*

Since it would seem that aromatic substances can only interfere with the oral action of remedies, there would seem to be no theoretical objection to such topical mixtures, provided, of course, that the actions of the constituents are neither antidotal nor inimical.

(7) *What is the relevance of natural potentisation to the origin and development of living organisms?*

The sustained natural potentisation of inorganic substances would require their presence in some dilution, the relative absence of sunlight, and some form of agitation, as from earth tremors. Such conditions have prevailed in former times upon the Earth. Though purely speculative, it might be suggested that the water, thus potentised, could induce the development of organic materials from the necessary elements, and further induce the development of cellular forms. The question is: which element, elements, or inorganic compounds might be implicated in this process? My own view, for what it is worth, is to look no further than *sulphur*. Substances of this nature, although usually regarded as highly insoluble in water, may produce colloidal suspensions which are more readily potentised than ionic solutions. Despite the fact that the molecules are aggregated within the colloidal suspension, thus effectively reducing the number of solute particles available for collision, the lack of true hydration shell formation improves the results of agitation.

The efficacy of homoeopathy has been demonstrated conclusively in clinical trials, and the measurable action of remedies upon enzymes and cellular cultures is indisputable. That it exists as a real phenomenon has been demonstrated, therefore, both *in vivo* and *in vitro*. Is it not time that the emotive, irrational and inquisitional views of those of capacious, but restricted, intellect were relegated, at last, to the unfathomable swamp of decaying absurdity?

Bibliography

The following is a selection of the papers and books which have been consulted in the preparation of the text:

1. Antonchenko VY, Ilyin VV. Points at issue in the physics of water and homoeopathy. British Homoeopathic Journal. April 1992, Vol. 81, pp. 9 1–93.
2. Atkins PW. Molecules. 1987. Freeman, New York.
3. Atkins PW. Quanta: A Handbook of Concepts. 2nd edition. 1991. Oxford University Press.
4. Barker R. LM Potencies. 2nd edition (revised). The Homoeopathic Supply Company. 1992.
5. Berezin AA. Isotopical Positional Correlations as a Possible Model for Benveniste Experiments. Medical Hypotheses. 1990, 31, pp. 43–45.
6. Boiron J, Vinh LD. Contribution to the Study of the Physical Structure of Homoeopathic Dilutions by Raman Laser Effect. Hahnemannian Gleanings. October 1976, pp. 455–467.
7. Callinan P. The Mechanism of Action of Homoeopathic Remedies – Towards a Definite Model. Journal of Complementary Medicine. July 1985, pp. 35–56.
8. Callinan P. Vibratory Energy in Water: A Model for Homoeopathic Action. Journal of Complementary Medicine. February 1986, pp. 34–53.
9. Davenas E, Beauvais F, Amara J, *et al.* Human basophil degranulation triggered by very dilute antiserum against IgE. Nature. 1988, 333, pp. 816–818.
10. Del Giudice E. Superradiance: A new approach to coherent dynamical behaviors of condensed matter. Center for Frontier Sciences. Fall/Winter 1990. Vol. 1, 2, pp. 16–17.
11. Endler P. Aspects of information storage and structures in water. British Homoeopathic Journal. October 1989, Vol. 78, pp. 253–254.
12. Florence AT, Attwood D. Physicochemical Principles of Pharmacy. 2nd edition. 1988. Macmillan.
13. Franks F. Water. Royal Society of Chemistry. 1st edition (revised). 1984.
14. Goodman Gilman A, Goodman LS, Gilman A. The Pharmacological Basis of Therapeutics. 6th edition. 1980. Macmillan.
15. Grange JM, Denman AM. Microdose-mediated immune modulation. British Homoeopathic Journal. April 1993, Vol. 82, pp. 113–118.

16. Hahnemann S. Organon of Medicine (6th edition): a new translation. 1983. Victor Gollancz.
17. Jain DVS, Jauhar SP. Physical Chemistry. 1988. Tata McGraw-Hill.
18. Mallove EF. Fire from Ice. 1991. John Wiley.
19. Némethy G, Scheraga HA. Structure of Water and Hydrophobic Bonding in Proteins. I: A Model for the Thermodynamic Properties of Liquid Water. Journal of Chemical Physics. June 15, 1962, Vol. 36, No. 12, pp. 3382–3399.
20. Popp FA. Some elements of homoeopathy. British Homoeopathic Journal. July 1990, Vol. 79, pp. 161–166.
21. Resch G, Gutmann V, Schauer H. The 'Shaking Effect' on the Conductivities of Liquids. Journal of Indian Chemistry Society. February 1982, Vol. LIX, pp. 130–133.
22. Resch G, Gutmann V. Structure and System Organisation of Homoeopathic Potencies. Berlin Journal on Research in Homoeopathy. September/December 1991, Vol. 1, No. 4/5, pp. 229–235.
23. Rubik B. The perennial challenge of anomalies at the frontiers of science. British Homoeopathic Journal. July 1994, Vol. 83, pp. 155–166.
24. Sharma RR. Scientific bases of dynamisation. Hahnemannian Gleanings. 1982, Vol.49, pp. 14–24.
25. Sharma RR. Homoeopathy today, a scientific appraisal. British Homoeopathic Journal. October 1986, Vol. 75, No. 4, pp. 231–237.
26. Sharma RR. Molecular Basis of Homoeopathy. Homoeopathy International. May 1990, pp. 16–19.
27. Smith C. Electromagnetic phenomena in biological systems and their relationship to allergic responses. British Homoeopathy Research Group. Communication No. 14. August 1985, pp. 36–40.
28. Smith C, Best S. Electromagnetic Man. 1989. Dent.
29. Smith RB Jr, Boericke G. Modern instrumentation for the evaluation of homoeopathic drug structure. Hahnemannian Gleanings. 1974, Vol. 41, pp. 99–119.
30. Winter MJ. Chemical Bonding. 1994. Oxford University Press.

Index